TODD WESTBROOK is a career j̶ enough to have worked for n and online outlets in a variety range of subject areas. More published under his byline across news, features, analysis and long-form pieces. His adopted home is in the Scottish Highlands. @tswstbrk tswestbrook.com

First published 2020

ISBN: 978-191302-552-6

Printed and bound by Clays Ltd., Bungay.

Typeset in 10.5 point Sabon and Frutiger
by Main Point Books, Edinburgh.

Revolution

A short, sharp history of Scottish wind power
– and where it goes in the future

TODD WESTBROOK

Luath Press Limited

EDINBURGH

www.luath.co.uk

For J

For the obvious reasons
And the not so obvious reasons

Contents

Foreword

CONSIDER THIS A health warning: what you are about to read is not intended as a dry, dispassionate, unopinionated discourse on every facet of the Scottish wind industry between ground zero and the present day. If that were the case, this book would be called *The Scottish Wind Industry 1950–2020*. I will leave that title to the academics.

Granted, I spent more than 15 years of my life providing fact-based, news-driven coverage of the wind revolution in Scotland, and elsewhere around the globe, for a leading in-dustry-focused publication. It was not a trade paper nor did it feature the evangelical campaigning favoured by many renew-able energy publishers; the starting point for my journalism was not 'wind is fantastic' but simply 'wind is…' – good, bad and/or ugly could be appended by the reader, as dictated by the information involved.

Coverage was neutral and any comment was clearly labelled and confined to the leader column, but nevertheless written with the subscriber – essentially those involved in the renewable energy sector – in mind. The publication was never fawning but it was serving a readership paying for market intelligence, and even opinion had to contribute towards that end. Yes, my personal political views snuck into print every now and again (from Scottish independence to Brexit, US trade policy to European bureaucracy), but even deeply held beliefs were framed and restrained by the needs of the paying public. No grandstand soapboxing from me.

A fierce devotion to telling the whole story simultaneously won friends and made enemies. Po-faced corporates were generally unimpressed with my efforts, however factual. Those with wider horizons and longer-term concerns understood that information is a necessary driver of learning and improvement, although perhaps that flatters me. In the end, I was really just trying to provide news that had not been reported elsewhere; if it was something that somebody, somewhere, did not want to see in print, as the saying goes, it probably had a better chance of making the front page.

What was not possible in the day-in-day-out grind of life as a beat reporter, later editor, was long-term perspective. That was not just a matter of time, of which there was never enough, it was more because providing context to a complex beast evolving over decades involves, by the very nature of the task, a prism of subjectivity. My old-fashioned journalistic creed considered any such intrusion an anathema; the more than a million words published under my byline never featured the first person pronoun outside of quotation marks.

This book is different. It is a personal, narrative history of a part of modern Scottish life that was centre stage for much of my professional career. The words that follow are about making sense of the milestones, roadblocks and wider achievements that make up one of the more remarkable social and economic events of the last 25 years. There was a time in the not so distant past when there were zero commercial wind turbines in Scotland; that there are now thousands deserves some consideration, particularly given the challenges looming in the shape of increasing energy demands and the ever-more acute climate crisis.

From the outset, it will be clear that I am no expert. I do, however, know who those experts are and where to find them, and it is largely they who tell the story you are about to read. But I am also there. Yes, everything that follows is, to the best of my ability, factual and faithfully represented. I have attributed sources when necessary and where possible without disrupting the flow of the narrative, but steered clear of footnotes. Nothing is imagined, assumed or extrapolated, but rather based on source materials or first-hand experiences. If there are any inaccuracies or misreadings they are not intentional but they are my responsibility, and I apologise in advance should that turn out to be the case.

This is, after all, a story of my telling; I have picked out what I believe is important, those moments that seem pivotal, those events that shaped what was to come. The people on the pages to come were not chosen at random; they have been allowed, even encouraged, to put forward their unadulterated and unchallenged beliefs, recollections and opinions. A different author, having selected a different series of guides, would likely follow a radically different trail of crumbs through the same forest of facts. I do, however, believe any chronicler would arrive at the same destination.

The timeline of this history starts with a revolutionary experiment on Orkney at the start of the 1950s. It concludes with profound questions about the sort of Scotland we want to live in, questions that would not have been asked 25 years ago. I suppose that must be considered progress of sorts.

Note: In a bid to address a few common myths and misconceptions about wind power, this book features a scavenger hunt of relatively unscientific and very personal responses to a dozen of the concerns most regularly raised about the sector in Scotland either during official discourse or when having a casual but suddenly interrupted drink at a nearby bar.

Introduction

MEGAWATTS, KILOWATT-HOURS, ASYNCHRONOUS generators and carbon paybacks will sometimes take centre stage in this short, sharp history of Scottish wind power but have no fear: the journey you will take over the following pages is not predominantly scientific, industrial or mechanical. It is human.

It is about saving the planet and living in the kind of world we always imagined; it is about a country moving away from smog, nuclear waste, leaky pipelines and slag heaps (bings, if you are local). It is about endlessly drawing power from the air around us and addressing global warming and being 'green' – whatever that actually means.

A certain amount of terminology is, however, necessary to explain the highways and byways of Scotland's wind power story over the last 25 years and as with all journeys some patience will be required as we travel from A to B. The final destination will be worth the investment of time, energy and vocabulary; trust me.

It must nevertheless be acknowledged, particularly in this age of digital navigation aids, that many readers will require a sneak-peek at the bigger picture – an overview of the route ahead – to establish a feeling from the outset for that winding blue line of travel, a sense of where the pilot is going to take us and what roads are going to feature along the way, in order to judge for themselves the commitment necessary.

Wind as a source of power has been with mankind for many thousands of years, harnessed for transport through the medium of the sail or translated via rotating 'arms' to drive millstones and draw water. Ruins of effective early installations can be found globally from the Middle East to

Asia and across Europe, where their impact stretches to art and literature. Windmills feature most famously in *Don Quixote* by Cervantes but also caught the imagination of writers Robert Louis Stevenson, Hilaire Belloc and even Shakespeare; artists moved by their countenance – to various degrees of obsession – include Van Gogh, Monet, Constable, Renoir, Rembrandt, Gauguin and van Ruisdael. Many pre-industrial structures are still with us, having largely been converted into tourist attractions, housing, restaurants or bars.

Making the jump from brute force to the creation of electricity came fairly late in the day via pioneering efforts in the 19th century, after which small wind turbines became commonplace in the US in the 1900s to supply farms in remote areas with light and other amenities (the installation at the beginning of the *Wizard of Oz*, before it leaps into its Technicolor phase, perfectly captures the concept). The era of commercial windpower, driven by early experiments with turbines connected to the main grid supply network – including one in Scotland – would arrive in the 1970s starting in California.

In Europe, the Danes and the Germans led an initial charge in the 1980s with communities and non-utilities the main proponents; it was more of an environmental and rural movement than strictly speaking a 'business' and deployments were often approached on an experimental basis with the aim of advancing the technology. Egalitarian, you could almost say.

Vintage machines were nothing like the graceful structures in most modern projects, painstakingly arrayed in an eye-pleasing matrix that tumbles rhythmically with the breeze. Instead the landscape of the 1970s and early 1980s featured squatty, short-armed and often crowded turbines spinning on a sometimes wobbly axis at unfathomable speed. Two blades, three blades, facing into the wind, facing away from the wind, perched on top of lattices, wooden poles or towers made of concrete, maybe of steel segments reinforced with metal strapping; it was at times a hodgepodge.

Early machines were often called 'tractors in the sky' by the northern European farmers who regularly played host; that is how robust and uncomplicated – perhaps workmanlike – the inner workings of the generators were. The oldest operational machine still in existence is thought to the be Tvindkraft prototype turbine on the west coast of Denmark, which went into service in 1978 and is still chugging along with the gales tumbling in off the North Sea. That machine is not unique in its effective antiquity; it remains quite common when travelling across Europe to come across machines built in the 1980s and even now reliably producing power.

They are not alone; wind deployments across Europe ramped up in breathtaking fashion through the 1990s, smashing through the 10 gigawatt barrier in 2000 – enough to power around seven million homes – and approaching a remarkable 20 times that number as 2020 began.

For a small corner of the globe, Scotland plays a not insignificant part in the bigger picture: the more than 9,000 megawatts of total wind power installed as of the end of 2019 is on a per-capita basis roughly 4.6 times the European average – 1,698 megawatts per million residents, compared with 378 megawatts/million across the EU – and tops the league tables well ahead of the next-best performer Denmark which boasts around 1,000 megawatts per million of its wind-loving citizens.

Put another way, for every man, woman or child living in Scotland, all 5.4 million of us, there is the equivalent of a very small wind turbine producing 1.7 kilowatts of electricity, enough to power an average domestic (relatively power-hungry) dishwasher. And that adds up to a *lot* of dishwashers, nearly two square kilometres of dishwashers if you packed them closely together or, if you stack them up, a pillar of dinner service cleanliness stretching 4,590km into the sky.

The figures – about wind, not white goods – will catch many by surprise. While it is widely acknowledged that Scotland has a healthy renewable energy industry, the specific statistics about its place in the big bad world are too often hidden within UK-wide numbers, which, while not inconsiderable in their own right, are not in fact as impressive as what is going on north of the border. The situation is of course complicated and sometimes muddied by a shared UK electricity network, which allows for easy and sometimes direct export of Scottish wind power to points south, and a policy, subsidy and regulatory environment that splits responsibility – and so credit and/or blame – between London and Edinburgh. But that should not distract from what has been achieved.

It is also worth emphasising that the country's phenomenal success, and this is crucial, must not be used as an excuse by policymakers to down tools. In the world of ten or even five years ago, there could have been a healthy debate about such a thing as 'too much wind power'; in the era of the climate emergency, that has all changed.

The warnings of what happens if we continue to overheat our planet are familiar and regularly encompass floods, fires, famine and disease, among other nightmares. So catastrophic are some predictions that the human brain simply fails to take in additional information beyond 'it's gonna be bad'. Yet even the widespread societal acceptance of the latter sentiment is an improvement on where were just a few years ago, an evolution from 'we really should get around to doing something' and a million miles from 'the jury is still out on climate change'.

And the realisation of just how bad things are is accelerating at an increasing rate. There is every chance the recent government-imposed deadline of 2045 for net zero emissions in Scotland (five years later for the UK as a whole) could be accelerated and, in any case, it is always good to get ahead of the curve given margins of error, room to manoeuvre etc. Every day that emissions are not reduced is a day wasted, every policy can kicked down the road is another scoop of coal on the planetary fire, each personal decision taken without reducing

Installed Wind Power on Per Capita Basis

Country	Population (million)	Installed Megawatts*	Per capita (MW/ million)
Scotland	5.4	9,171	1,698
Denmark	5.8	6,128	1,057
Sweden	10.2	8,985	881
Ireland	4.9	4,115	840
Germany	83	61,357	739
Spain	46.9	25,808	550
Portugal	10.3	5,437	528
Norway	5.3	2,444	461
Finland	5.5	2,284	415
EU (ex UK)	445.8	168,716	378
Austria	8.9	3,159	355
Belgium	11.5	3,879	337
Greece	10.7	3,576	334
Netherlands	17.3	4,600	266
France	67	16,646	248
UK (ex Scotland)	61.2	14,344	234
Italy	60.4	10,512	174
Poland	38	5,917	156
Romania	19.4	3,029	156

*Feb 2020 statistics from WindEurope, except Scotland and rUK which are Sept 2019 figures from UK Govt.

our individual carbon footprint is the result of false logic, and perhaps immoral (if you want to have that philosophical argument with the person sitting next to you on the airplane); time is nigh and all that.

UK advisory body the Committee on Climate Change (CCC) stressed that very point in its 2019 Progress Report to the Scottish Parliament, in which it spelled out the need for 'urgent action' if net zero is to be achieved on schedule in 2045. 'Every sector of the economy must contribute fully,' it said.

Policies must be embedded across all levels of government with strong leadership and coordination at the centre, the CCC added, with the public engaged in the challenge and all actions designed with people at the heart: 'Policy should provide a clear and stable direction and a simply investable set of rules and incentives that leave room for businesses to innovate and find the most effective means of switching to low-carbon solutions.'

And the focus needs to be in the 2020s and 2030s, rather than farther down the line. Electric vehicles, green buildings, emission-lite agriculture, tree planting and peatland restoration, low-carbon heat, decarbonisation infrastructure (CO_2 transport and storage, hydrogen clusters, renewable electricity support), lifestyle changes: all according to the CCC are needed today.

They are not alone in the call to arms or in taking up an increasingly common refrain: in the crisis facing all of us there is no longer such a thing as too many solutions. We no longer have the luxury of choice when it comes to decarbonisation, we are going to need to full complement of human endeavour and ingenuity to salvage the planet that we have fucked up – that we continue to fuck up. Which makes it both odd and disconcerting that Scotland is not talking more about the easy win already spinning on horizons around the country, even if wind power makes some segments of the population uncomfortable in terms of knee-jerk opposition.

Edinburgh artist and poet Alec Finlay has long been intrigued by the interface between people, landscape and technological change, including renewable energy, and is not alone in believing the current crisis radically changes the baseline of the debates ahead, and the choices to be made as a result. 'We are so far beyond arguments about whether or not people like wind,' he said. 'Do people like having a washing machine, do they like driving a car? That's the way they need to start thinking about it. Those are the sort of choices you have to make in a war, and climate is now a war.'

Anyone involved in even a tangential way with the wind industry will have some experience of the atmosphere created after being asked 'And what do you do?' at a dinner party, wedding reception or in fact any social gathering where diverse groups of people gather around a single table. The entirely innocent question, when answered by those designing, developing, building or supplying the most visible of renewable energy technologies, inevitably results in misunderstandings from some around the table, awkward avoidance from others and outright hostility from a few.

The revelation – and this holds true in the pub, on the bus or at the school gates – is capable of generating the sort of reception usually reserved for those involved in the arms industry, the taxman (or woman), traffic wardens and tabloid journalists. Occasionally heated conversations based on misinformation and hostility can follow, roping in money, politics and climate science (and/or denial) along the way.

This does not extend to other renewables technologies to the same degree: solar power is generally better understood and more accepted, marine deployments of wave and tidal are seen as plucky, warm and fuzzy (like seals or puffins, but producing electricity), while bio-generators such as anaerobic digestion, co-firing and biomass tend to fly under the public perception radar.

Traditional generators do catch their fair share of flak, of course: nuclear has long been capable of dividing the room, coal's days are numbered, people can get very worked up

Eye of the beholder: turbines in the Scottish landscape, like this array at Beinn Ghlas near Taynuilt in Argyll, are seen by some as proof positive that the country is taking a pragmatic approach to the climate challenge, while others believe that wind farms are a blot on the landscape.

© Leeming + Paterson Photography

about large hydro-electric dams flooding valleys and forcing out communities while swallowing habitats. (On the flip side, you do not often see bare-knuckle confrontations about the rights or wrongs of combined-cycle gas turbines.)

Wind, however, is uniquely and stubbornly emotive. Some of that is about money, on which more anon, but more often it is down to visuals, views and vistas; which is why any discussion about wind must necessarily be seen in the context of Scotland's relationship with its landscape.

The country, despite one of the most concentrated and iniquitous patterns of land ownership in Europe, has a romantic but nevertheless tangible attachment to the prospect and heritage of mountain and glen, loch and river, island and coastline. A particular estate laird or national body may strike a deal to allow a wind farm to be developed on his/her/its acreage, but it is the population as a whole that accommodates the resulting impact on views – which most would probably agree belong to all rather than one.

This 'it is ours' mentality, particularly in the Highlands and Islands, has roots that stretch deep into the social structure developed through the clan system, strengthened by an increasingly urban population's relationship with the ties represented by 'the outdoors', and reinforced in recent years by the right to roam, which came into being in 2005 and allows for open access outwith some very narrow bands of restriction. And an individual need not be actively tramping the hills to feel that sense of collective ownership; it is part of the national DNA across locals, commuters, staycationers, crofters and city-dwellers. Any project that flirts with even a marginally iconic landscape risks howls of protest from near and far in Scotland and from the diaspora elsewhere in the UK and globally. The sense of loss can be real, even if occasionally overblown or – in some instances – adopted for convenience.

That is the main reason, although certainly not the only reason, that feelings about renewables and wind power run so deep and sometimes dark and can colour all related conversations, be those in the supermarket checkout queue or in Parliament. And however elaborate the argument against a given wind farm, more often than not at its heart is that visceral dislike of the way it looks. That is why in Scotland, a full 25 years on from the first deployment of the commercial wind era, the sector remains a hot-button topic and the subject of ongoing misinformation, much mythology and basic misunderstandings of its role in a national energy system racing to adapt to the demands of the climate emergency.

It can be a hard sell. People opposed to wind cling to dogmatic perceptions like a cherished childhood teddy bear and the more the baseline changes, the deeper the fingers dig into the faux fur and stuffing. Never mind the ever-steeper requirements to curb global temperatures, the increasing demands of electrification and the no-show by other would-be low-carbon technology solutions: the vocal minority who hated wind back in the day generally hate it now.

For those so inclined, the prospect of just about any turbine being built in just about any location fuels a near-apoplectic reaction and a flurry of letter writing, reason be damned and roll on with the hyperbole: wind is too ugly, expensive, loud and inefficient; it is a con, produces more carbon than it saves, makes you sick and lowers your house price. It culls countless birds, scares away tourists and nobody likes turbines anyway. (For the record, none of those things are true. Check out the Wind Myths throughout the book for additional detail, with the usual health warnings.)

One long-time veteran of what amounts to the frontline of the wind farm battle – the 'public exhibition' meetings held in village halls, country hotels or sports centre at which locals are introduced to the specifics of a planned project – has spent decades fighting the industry's corner. 'I can in some way understand the negative reactions,' said the community engagement expert. 'There has been very little change in the

Scottish landscape over many, many decades and suddenly there is this new element on the horizon.'

In her experience, the loudest anti voices are split between two distinct and sometimes overlapping groups: 'There is definitely an older generation that has severe doubts about climate change and so opposes any attempt to address that; and then there is another and often related group that has moved to a given area from other places and want it to stay the same, want to see their views protected because that is the reason they came. The wider message of why change is now absolutely necessary perhaps hasn't gotten through.'

For the latter group it is not just wind farms; grain silos, woodchip hoppers, petrol stations and housing are also in the firing line. And it matters not if a particular project meets with constantly evolving guidance on visual impacts produced by local authorities, national guidelines and/or statutory consultees.

Our engagement expert, based on years of experience, suggests that the need to embrace the low carbon economy, and wind's role in that fight, is either intentionally tuned out or perhaps is simply not being effectively communicated by social and political interests outside the renewable energy industry, perpetuating the illusion that climate change is always someone else's problem. 'The onshore antis will often point to offshore wind as a better way forward. But that is an unsustainable position; we need every technology, and we need more of them.'

Profit provides another axe to grind. 'Those opposed often complain that they are paying for the renewable energy revolution through their electricity bills and with an altered aspect out of their front windows, while wind companies get all the benefits in terms of revenue. They don't recognise, or perhaps do not accept, the wider societal benefits.'

Some detect signs of movement. A second front-line campaigner, with a different company, believes the post-2015 shift away from government support mechanisms, and an increasing acknowledgement that onshore wind is the lowest-cost generation technology available in the UK, has made the technology more palatable to a wider slice of the population. 'In the early days many people were convinced that their hard earned cash was going into the industry's pockets for no return, but with the end of the subsidy era those arguments have shifted, there is now a better understanding of the benefits and role of the wind sector.'

And that knowledge extends to the wider energy mix, she believes. 'Take the Torness nuclear power plant and the neighbouring wind farms near Edinburgh: for a long time there was no concept of what was going on inside that giant concrete box, no big green/red light on the outside to say whether it was generating or not. People just assumed it was working even when it wasn't. But as soon as one turbine stopped spinning that raised questions about the effectiveness of wind in general.'

A post-war generation raised on electricity provided by large, distant power stations – out of sight, out of mind – remains immune to the idea that all technologies have their pros and cons, problems and advantages; as long as the living room light goes on when the switch is thrown, we'll be fine. Younger people schooled in the stark demands of the climate emergency arguably have a better grasp of the subtleties and have the ability to see a bigger picture when it comes to how we power our world.

And they do no not necessarily have to be part of Extinction Rebellion to counterbalance the *Escape to the Country* mindset; many of the families stretching back generations in the same town, the same farm, the same croft are equally adept at understanding the inevitability of change in the countryside, the trade-offs necessary for survival in the face of challenges like the climate fight, as the youth facing a life filled with the negatives of global warming. Even the hippies will have their

Californication: the image of wind as sometimes portrayed in the mainstream UK press is unrepresentative and out of date. This array near Palm Springs, while still operational, was constructed in the 1980s and bears no resemblance to modern equivalents.
© Todd Westbrook

say, according to our initial community engagement expert: 'For renewable energy as a whole, and in Scotland in particular, there are still the idealists necessary to keep the vision and the business sides of the equation in balance. That will remain crucial going forward.'

All of which provides reason to be cheerful, perhaps, amid the current doldrums of UK energy policy. 'This game isn't over; you have to be an optimist,' she said.

Which is not to let the wider green lobby off the hook, because the exaggeration barometer deployed by the antis also swings the opposite way: to some of those in favour, particularly on the campaigning side of the climate message, wind is often painted as the hassle-free fast-lane to carbon salvation and the cure for all emission evils. That turbine, any turbine, is the answer; throw your support behind wind and feel free to ignore the more complicated questions of how to reset the rest of the energy industry, how to wean ourselves off fossil fuels, the best way to support decentralised, decarbonised power and the inevitable losers from that transition – because there are already, and will continue to be, those that pay the

MYTH 1

Wind is ugly

Depends on who you ask, and whether they are looking at an actual Scottish wind farm or a stock image of some of the rusted, ramshackle and abandoned projects built in southern California in the 1980s, which are often used to illustrate negative news stories about wind. UK government figures regularly show a majority surveyed would be happy to have a large-scale renewable energy project in their area, although they do not ask specifically about the aesthetics of onshore wind. For a comparison, it is worth considering the visuals of a wind turbine next to a fossil fuel plant, a coal mine, a radioactive waste storage facility. Eye of the beholder and all that.

necessary price of our inevitable global shift away from carbon. And that could get really ugly as the urgency of our situation increases.

So, the truth of wind power in Scotland is complicated, subtle and somewhere between the doom and gloom of the naysayers and the sunny uplands described by the industry itself. It has been influenced by ever-shifting government policy, market reaction to those parameters, the tendency of investment to follow profit curves and the inevitable hurdles and problems created by a fast-moving technology sector. It is muddied by devolution and constitutional politics, by national industrial history, sense of self, a tradition of maximising resources, changing population profiles and by cross-border bodies weighted towards broader UK interests.

Wind is simultaneously, and despite strong feelings from the pro and anti brigades, somewhat of a blindspot on the national stage; that the first commercial Scottish project is 25 years old in 2020 seems to have escaped just about everyone's notice, that wind sparked a revolution in how this country produces its electricity seems wildly under-valued, that it has gone from nothing to Scotland's largest source of generation in terms of both output and capacity is for many a revelation.

Part of that is driven by the news agenda: innovation makes a great story and features strong visuals, so our screens and print media are filled with the promise of fantastical wave and tidal machines, of photovoltaic windows and bricks that will magically generate electricity, of towering offshore turbines being installed in a sparkling North Sea by gleaming, futuristic vessels christened with names that would not be out of place in an Avengers movie: Thor, Brave Tern, Apollo, Orion. The focus on what comes next, rather than what we already know, is sharpened by trade bodies and industry associations looking to government to secure funding to develop new technologies, for a guaranteed route to market in a risky world, for an edge in an ever more competitive business climate. The workhorses of renewables, which in Scotland means onshore wind, are less sexy. Land-based turbines involve mud and bulldozers and construction workers with tattoos. Gritty and real; governments are not splashing cash on that, television networks and newspaper editors are uninterested. Public attention drifts elsewhere.

Yet the 'boring' part of this story requires telling. A quarter-century of pioneering, dogged application not only resulted in massive advances in the Scotland's wind sector – from noise mitigation to better understanding bird behaviours, from bigger, more efficient turbines to sophisticated control systems, from lasers to logistics – but also quietly forced the evolution and/or creation of a grid network, workforce, planning system, utility sector and policy environment fit and ready to help meet the challenges of the climate emergency.

And it can be done better, there are still improvements to be made; there were things that went right over the first 25 years but no one should pretend that everything was perfect. There are some wind farms where wind farms probably should not be, the planning system at times put an unnecessary brake on progress and there was not enough done to promote landmark manufacturing investment (largely because Scotland and the UK are really bad at playing the state aid game). Other items also make the 'room to improve' list: too little profit was shared on a local, regional and national basis, community initiatives too often played second-fiddle to the commercial sector, rival renewable energy technologies were starved of early-stage investment oxygen on the grounds of austerity, not nearly enough attention was paid to green heat and transport, energy storage was an afterthought.

Much of the criticism can be traced to what became the compartmentalisation of wind power: the rapid success of the technology gave decision makers at all levels the opportunity to tick the 'low carbon' box without looking too far into what else was required in terms of social acceptance, without an overview of the impacts on the national built and natural environment, without considering system-wide implications of the shift away from fossil fuel generation. It also, according to some critics, allowed the wind industry to operate in isolation, largely remote from the need to integrate more effectively with its its human, societal and physical surroundings.

Edinburgh artist and poet Finlay once again: 'Ownership is a crucial issue that is not being dealt with enough. Wind works well in places like Orkney because its relationship with the people is more progressive and the community is more educated about renewables. Of course there are still conflicts but the developers and the engineers are mainly from the island and can resolve those down at the pub. It just functions better.'

Wind power, he argued, should have been and in future should be part of a longer-term vision for the country and its landscape, as part of a national and more nationalised effort to tackle decarbonisation. Finlay said this would require blurred boundaries and include rewilding, tree-planting, recreation and conservation alongside and even within wind developments; turbines amid woods, trails, ponds and in a plan designed more for 100 years than just the two or three decade lifespan of the turbines. He suggests that wind has in many respects been the hard-edged forestry plantation of renewable energy technologies; an out-of-date monoculture approach to national-scale development that blots out all else.

That is already changing in parts; newbuild wind farms are without fail designed with an element of battery storage included, so potentially mitigating those times when the breeze does not blow or the demand dips, while at least one major utility is exploring the co-location of solar arrays within existing wind projects. Finlay would no doubt argue it is a good start, if still somewhat short of true integration outwith the energy spectrum.

Expertise of all stripes will be required and will offer a chance for more established industries to play their part.

'We need oil and gas to be part of this transition, to come along on the journey to a clean, green future,' said our second engagement expert. 'They can help to decide what this future looks like and they have the finance, experience and track record of innovation necessary to make sure it happens. Government can help with that coming together.'

Cooperation within renewables is also important, she added, saying industry needs to learn the lessons of the early years when fierce competition was perhaps counterproductive to the outlook of the wind sector as a whole. 'Working together we are far more powerful than when we work alone,' she said. 'Other industries are much better at that; if we had each given a little something in some situations, we would have gotten a lot more somewhere else.'

One of those benefits might have been more substantial investment in the supply chain. Jobs have certainly been created over the last 25 years, tens of thousands of them, but the headline-grabbing factory employing many thousands at a single site, the sort of facility that politicians can tour wearing hi-vis vests and hardhats, has been notable by its absence, by the short or troubled lifespan of the few exceptions. In part this is due to a wider shift across the UK from making things to talking about things, about shuffling papers rather than animating blueprints. It is also symptomatic of a global drift towards outsourcing labour-intensive fabrication industries to far-flung ports. Governments in Edinburgh and London will have to do better at either explaining why this tide cannot be meaningfully resisted, or putting in place a better set of policies to mitigate against.

Finally, the details of what happened over the last 25 years are important; on behalf of society, governments and politicians are taking difficult decisions on the winding, uphill road to net zero. Actions to date have ranged across the spectrum from expedient to disingenuous, more often than not plagued by the short-termism that is inherent in modern social discourse.

For too many years, to be seen to be doing something *now* has been more important than being effective in the longer term; for much of the last quarter-century the focus has been firmly on which finger to put in the hole, rather than on the rising water about to overspill the top of the dyke.

There is no longer the option of ignoring the more difficult side of that Low Country equation. It has gone beyond just stopping the leaks – one finger will not do the trick. And because time is short, there is little margin for error; the actions taken today, the decisions reached and how they are implemented, will determine whether it is possible to avoid a tipping point beyond which climate chaos will be unavoidable and catastrophic.

This will not be easy; in the energy sector – just one element of the climate riddle – Scotland has over a quarter-century witnessed a shift from community to large-scale commercial onshore wind, a would-be boom in offshore wind that was largely over before it began, a similarly doomed surge in marine technologies, a second offshore wind surge that is only now gaining momentum, and finally a Westminster-induced coma that shut down the majority of new onshore wind projects and from which the industry is only now, in 2020, starting to show some signs of recovery.

No one can afford such a start-stop narrative and, as constitutional battles rumble on, the Scottish government must realise that it is not good enough to blame London for inaction in hopes of a brighter, more independent day; Edinburgh can and must do more with the powers that it already has. Our second engagement expert again: 'Policy levers can be pulled in Holyrood to make it more beneficial for projects to be based here. For example, the cost of building any renewable energy project is inflated by up to 15 per cent due to measures completely within the control of Scottish ministers.'

And that is just one example, she believes. There is plenty more than can be done without resort to those distant voices

Electricity Demand Provided by Wind Power

Country	% of electricity demand provided by wind*
Austria	13
Belgium	10
Denmark	48
EU (ex UK)	15
Finland	7
France	7
Germany	26
Greece	12
Ireland	33
Italy	7
Netherlands	12
Norway	4
Poland	9
Portugal	27
Romania	11
Scotland	50
Spain	21
Sweden	15
UK (ex Scotland)	18

* Based on February 2020 statistics from WindEurope, except Scotland and rUK which are based on December 2019 figures from Scottish Government. Statistics provided by Holyrood for Scotland/rUK are not directly comparable with the European equivalent, so an admittedly unsatisfactory but necessary 'average' has been adopted that reflects the 'gross electricity consumption' figure of 56.5% and the 'electricity consumption by fuel' figure of 43.1%.

south of the border; the key outcome, whatever the level of government, must be meaningful contributions to the wider cause. The byword in every case needs to be momentum. An end goal will help; for wind power, stipulating that Scotland must in the next ten years replace 3,000 long-in-the-tooth turbines with more efficient, more powerful modern machines, while building 2,000 new generators onshore and a further 1,000 offshore – for example – does not guarantee such an outcome, but it does provide a rough indication of the direction of travel that all should be working towards and paves the way to meeting 100 per cent of ever-increasing electricity demands from renewable energy. Other options, different approaches and tweaks (down the line) are of course available, bar 'none of the above'.

Which is why what happened over the 25-year history of the commercial wind sector in a small storm-lashed country on the north-west fringe of Europe deserves telling: the successes and mistakes must be heeded, the pitfalls avoided, the lessons and learnings applied. The first generation of what amounts to a large-scale research and development programme needs to go to work for the people who helped to fund that valuable experience through their energy bills, needs to be re-invested in solutions that will in the longer term be of benefit to everyone in Scotland and beyond, whatever their views on wind power.

And if speeding up decarbonisation simultaneously makes the energy system more democratic and decentralised, more likely to benefit all-comers rather than just those wearing business attire, better tailored to the needs of communities as well as landowners, then so much the better.

Be under no illusions: the history that follows will not by itself solve the wider problems of a planet facing meltdown, and should not be used as an excuse for inaction on other fronts. At best, in fact, it will only help to define the tabs and blanks on a single piece of the 1,000-strong jigsaw that is the climate emergency. But perhaps what follows can help to kickstart discussions about part of the answer and, at least, means there are just 999 pieces to go.

What are you waiting for? Go on and accept the challenge that faces us all. Turn the page.

I

Testing a Theory

THE ENGINEERS WORKING far above Costa Head through storm season 1951–2 must have kept a weather eye open for sudden squalls blowing off the North Atlantic and across the main island of Orkney in the far north of Scotland.

Crew members dispatched by engineering specialist John Brown & Co in Glasgow were forbidden from climbing to the top of the open-air, seven-story lattice tower when average winds were stronger than 20 miles per hour (mph), but that would not have safeguarded against unexpected gusts.

They operated without ropes or safety harnesses, a health and safety regime captured by grainy black and white BBC footage in December that year and in archive photos from across the build. Nevertheless, if lack of reports to the contrary can be taken as proof, the workers in flat caps and fedoras, crombies and tweeds emerged unscathed during construction of Scotland's first modern wind turbine.

Previous breeze-blown efforts across the UK had served up small quantities of power for specific tasks largely for the benefit of remote estates, crofts and other small farms. The concept tested on Costa Head was designed to revolutionise rural life by supplying power at scale directly to the grid network, contributing to increasing demands from far-flung communities for the seemingly limitless electricity no longer given a second thought by those in urban Britain.

The Orkney machine, half galvanised prairie windmill and half steampunk blimp, blazed its trail for more than four years

Working at height: construction of the Costa Head turbine on Orkney in 1951.
With the kind permission of SSE plc

atop a 500-metre-high headland defined by ocean-plunging cliffs to the north and backed by the inland Loch of Swannay. The small islet of Eynhallow and the larger mass of Rousay neighboured across a green-blue sound to the north-east while, to the west, the Atlantic stretched all the way to North America.

EW Golding, an engineer and since 1948 head of rural electrification and wind power at the Electrical Research Association in London, selected the site for a prototype generator following a groundbreaking resource measurement campaign. That high-tech finger in the wind extended across 50 sites dotted along the exposed western edges of the United Kingdom.

Mawr in Caernarfonshire, north-west Wales, was top of the list in terms of raw potential but perhaps suffered when compared with the infrastructure and accessibility of its Scottish competition, which featured an existing stone and brick building at Costa Head and ready if rough access via roads and tracks. Average wind speeds at the site were estimated at 25mph when measured at ten feet off the ground, which in modern terms and without going too far into the lingo and science, would be classified in the highest category of resource.

Golding was on a mission reflected in parallel developments on the European continent and in the US under the umbrella of United Nations body UNESCO. He was convinced not only of the potential of wind as a power source but particularly how it could be applied in, and be of benefit to, rural economies and communities.

In the February 1955 edition of the Journal of the Institution of Electrical Engineers, he wrote with Pythia-like precision about the growing opportunity for wind technology, which 'lies partly in the increasing cost of power generation from fuels and in the realisation of the speed with which world supplies of these are being exhausted; partly in the desire of countries lacking fuels of their own to be independent of imports'.

He was convinced 'greatly increased knowledge of aerodynamics resulting from rapid advances in the aircraft industry' could be put to work in the generation of electricity.

The Englishman and his ERA colleagues split wind into three categories starting with small-scale applications for remote individual premises, through medium-sized machines like Costa Head designed to power isolated communities, up to large-scale applications that could 'feed their output directly into main electricity supply networks'.

Golding believed the economics could potentially be a challenge to both designer and end user but wrote positively of the resource available. 'Without doubt there is ample energy in the wind to meet the needs of scattered communities, in many parts of the world, which cannot be given power supplies from more conventional sources.'

He indicated, in language that applies equally to today's renewable energy market, that final costs would depend on 'the windiness of the site, which governs annual output per kilowatt installed, and upon the annual charges per kilowatt for interest, depreciation and maintenance, which are proportional to the capital cost of the plant'.

The ERA teamed up with the state-owned North of Scotland Hydro-Electric Board, responsible for supplying power to Orkney, to plan, manufacture and deploy the Costa turbine. The utility, perhaps due in part to links between Board Chief Executive Edward MacColl with the company where he was once employed, selected John Brown & Co to carry out the work.

MacColl, who had already championed the landmark Cruachan pumped-storage scheme in Argyll and Bute, had served his apprenticeship with the Clydebank fabricator. According to materials stored in the heritage department at hydro board successor SSE, the energy pioneer will almost certainly have been a – or perhaps the – main utility proponent of the Costa Head experiment.

The ERA itself was founded in 1920 to undertake investigations into technological innovation for manufacturers, suppliers and larger users of electricity. Work on wind for large-scale applications was supported by the Ministry of Fuel and Power while smaller deployments came under the auspices of the Ministry of Agriculture and Fisheries. Spending on the Costa Head deployment reached £4,799 through the end of 1951, according to Hydro Board documents, although no breakdown on the contributions from various participants is available. The equivalent spending today would be around £150,000 which compares very favourably to renewables demonstration projects of similar scale installed in more recent years.

John Brown & Co received the order to build the 100 kilowatt wind turbine, enough to power a small settlement or large farm complex, in 1949. The device was designed around an air-cooled generator within an organic art deco nacelle casing that featured few straight lines. Manchester company Metropolitan-Vickers Electrical – apologies in advance for the necessary diversion into techno-geekery – supplied the two-tonne, slip-ring heart of the machine, which produced power at 415 volts, three phase, 50 cycles.

Three compressed hardwood blades were in Golding's notation 'tapered, untwisted, free to drag and cone', governed by hydraulic pitch controls and positioned in relation to the wind direction by automatic electric weather-cocking. Each wing weighed 150 pounds and featured spars of compressed laminated wood, internal ribs of spruce and a mahogany veneer enclosed in plastic before being painted. The rotor measured 50 feet when the hardware was originally installed but, in reaction to the specific operational conditions at the site, blades were later shortened by five feet each and capacity further fine-tuned. The rounded front of the turbine faced into the wind with the blades spinning perpendicular to the ground at the rear of the streamlined device.

Completed components were crated in the west of Scotland and shipped to Orkney via Aberdeen before being loaded onto lorries covering the 19.5 miles from Kirkwall to the building site. The final stretch was little more than hill tracks made all but impassable whenever there was snow; tractors were on hand to ride to the rescue. The various elements of the 22-foot long turbine generator were assembled onsite and winched by hand to the top of a three-legged 72-foot tower using an elaborate set of ropeworks, galleys, cranes and cradles. A concrete block, piled firmly into the soft-rock Cost Head soil, was topped with a steel plate to serve as an anchor for each galvanised metal leg. Original timetables were delayed by weather but testing commenced around the tail-end of 1951.

Wind speeds in January of 1952 reached a sustained 125mph during a storm estimated to have caused £1 million in damages to Orkney – prompting a subsequent UK government promise of £20,000 in aid – with the Costa Head turbine losing the needle from its onboard wind speed indicator when it reached the maximum 120 mph setting and had nowhere else to go. By comparison, top operational speeds for the machine, when electricity could be safely produced at capacity, were between 35 and 60 mph. Anything beyond that range triggered an automatic shutdown.

The North of Scotland Hydro-Electric Board continued to road-test the technology, with John Brown & Co as project lead, through the end of 1956. At that stage, it became increasingly clear to the utility top brass that the cheaper and more reliable way to supply Orkney customers with electricity was to extend the island's grid network infrastructure. The demonstrator was handed over to the ERA and considered a failed experiment.

The engineers involved were disappointed. John Brown & Co project member Tom Mensforth, writing in Institution of Engineering and Technology publication Electronics and Power in 1976, unflatteringly described the 'lightness and fragility'

Job done: the precursor of today's commercial wind sector was only operational for a few years in the early 1950s at Costa Head on Orkney.
With the kind permission of SSE plc

of elements borrowed from the aviation sector as being one strand of a much wider series of issues. Failure of the project was attributed to:

> the aircraft design, the unsuitability for rough local conditions and particularly the inadequacy of the dampers, the weakness of the rotor/blade system operating with axis horizontal, oil contamination in the control gear, corrosion caused by the salt-laden air, and the remoteness of the site.

Furthermore:

> Pressure to complete meant vital parts were in hand before mating parts were developed, let alone detailed. The machine was too complicated: overmuch attention was given to exotic and academic considerations and insufficient to the practicability of design.

John Brown & Co did start preliminary work on a second-generation machine based on the Costa Head experience. The turbine was expected to be 2.5-times as powerful and would feature simplified internal engineering and two rather than three blades linked to a rocking yoke to mitigate wind gusts. It seems the device was never built.

Stromness-based wind engineer Richard Gauld, who we will meet properly in Chapter Eight and who has built many projects on the islands and elsewhere in Scotland, said with the benefit of hindsight that 'the chosen [Costa Head] site was perhaps too turbulent due to the high cliffs'; uneven airflows – think an airplane going over the mountains – will cause stresses and strains on any technology. Gauld said although the machine did not last very long it nevertheless 'proved that wind generation was viable in Orkney' and, by extension, across the UK.

Mensforth retired in 1960 with the gift of silver cigarette box engraved in perfunctory fashion with his name, dates of service and with the best wishes of John Brown & Co. He continued to believe in, and actively lobby for, the potential of wind power technology and in 1979 at the IEE Future Energy Concepts conference in London presented a next-generation 'big wheel' wind concept based on a 600-foot tall spoked turbine designed to power up to 15,000 homes. Partners John Laing Construction, Glasgow engineering company Howdens and state utility the Central Electricity Generating Board eventually carried out a joint study of the plans. A proposed prototype designed to power a more modest 2,000 houses was never produced.

Golding died in 1965 no doubt convinced of the merits of the technology he had been championing since 1948. Writing in the *Journal IEE* in 1955, with information from the Orkney trials most certainly at his fingertips, he forecast a bright future for wind power generally as a generation technology capable of undercutting more expensive alternatives. He more specifically supported the concept of the grid-connected turbine as first deployed at Costa Head, and which has reached thousands and thousands of installations in the UK alone and perhaps up to a million worldwide.

Golding wrote:

To judge the economy of using this energy its cost must be compared with that of power generation by alternative sources. This is very important. One can base a decision on what capital cost can be justified for a machine designed to operate in a given wind regime, only on a knowledge of this alternative cost. An annual average wind speed of 25mph and a capital cost of around £50 per kilowatt may be required where generator costs are low, but 15mph and £150 per kilowatt, or even more, may be satisfactory when the machine is in competition only with expensive means of power generation.

He added:

> It is already clear that wind power plants in the medium range of size, for which the scope is very large and widespread, can be manufactured at a cost low enough for them to compete favourably with diesel generation. No definite statement on the eventual cost of large installations can yet be made, although there is no reason to conclude that these will be uneconomically high.

Influential IET publication *Engineering*, reviewing the Costa Head experiment in an unbylined July 1955 article, offered a more qualified judgement:

> The main problem is essentially that the wind is a reliable source of energy but an unreliable source of power, and if wind machines are to be used to the best advantage they must incorporate some method of storage. Wind machines must first be a sound practical installation and it is not until they have worked on an operational site that they may be said to have proved themselves fully.

The exact fate of the Costa Head turbine is unclear. In 1956, control of the machine passed from the Hydro Board to the ERA, after which it seems to have simply faded out of the public eye. It has been referenced as 'dismantled' but whether it fell into disrepair, collapsed in a storm or was ultimately decommissioned in a systematic way – and exactly when – remains for now an unknown.

More certain is the experience the experiment provided

for engineers and the wider wind sector about commercial turbine applications, what Gauld described as 'a starting point for the industry in the UK'. Also certain is that the learnings – the endeavour and science and engineering deployed in the harshest of environments – would have to wait another 40 years before being successfully applied in a wider Scottish context. And even then the halcyon days for onshore wind power, which as you are about to learn were arguably among the most remarkable in the history of the electricity sector, would last just 20 years before returning to uncertainty, political squabbling and an uphill struggle for acceptance as a newbuild technology capable of meaningful contribution to the Scottish, UK and European energy mix.

2

The Scream and the strange birth of alternative energy in Scotland

THE HIGH-FLYING HISTORY of Scotland's commercial wind power sector starts rather closer to the ground; arguably with a single drop of water.

This precipitation fell onto already sodden earth in the south-west of the country and scrambled down through a vast catchment into a burn which tumbled across the hillside until it joined forces with other flows to form a small river.

The weight of this water, encouraged by the pull of gravity, gathered pace until, much closer to sea level, it was diverted into a man-made channel and funnelled via underground tunnels into a powerhouse and through a hydro-electric turbine.

Power created by the eventful journey of this liquid pioneer was, however, worth much less than that of equally travelled droplets which just happened to fall elsewhere across Scotland, into catchments feeding hydro stations owned by the country's two utility companies.

A subset intersection of long-time green power activists, emerging carbon neutralists and oft-ignored engineering visionaries believed the state of play discriminated against small producers, who also as it happened were what has since become known as 'environmentally friendly'. It also seemed fundamentally unfair. Surely translating the collected by-product of a rain-lashed climate at the north-west fringe of Europe into electricity, a sort of local-scale energy transubstantiation that for many represented the opening salvo of a wider green assault on the electricity sector,

Trickle down: the hydro sector in Scotland established both a tradition of maximising the country's natural resources and the need for appropriate market mechanisms to affect meaningful change.
© Todd Westbrook

should be better rewarded?

The post-privatisation electricity market of the early 1990s, led in Scotland by two newly-established corporations evolved from regional supply boards, was uninterested in the newcomers. There was little space for small, dispersed generation in a system built around coal, gas and nuclear power plants connected to market via trunk-road transmission lines. Residential consumers were in the main uncaring about what lay behind the light switch; industry and business was focused on the short-term bottom line of cheap electricity. For both sets of end users, it was largely damn the consequences: just ten years away from the 21st century, more than 70 per cent of UK electricity was still coal-fired, the majority from very large-scale plants.

Water, however, tends to erode even the most solid of foundations. Our undervalued droplet eventually wormed a channel into the Scottish electricity sector that wind power pioneers – in the shape of what one old-timer called a 'bunch of sandal-wearing, bearded academics; sidelined corporate middle management; and a shower of misfit hippies' – would turn into a torrent of turbines built over two decades, establishing a mainstream position in the country's increasingly diverse generation profile.

From the first commercially-produced Scottish wind power in 1995 to the final stages of the unprecedented building boom after 2015, billions would be invested, many thousands of jobs would be supported or created and a long-static energy sector would be revolutionised. Landscapes would be altered, societal and stakeholder faultlines created and political views challenged and shifted. Just as rapidly, in the years to 2020, the shift away from mainland wind projects and towards islands and offshore installations, as well as other low-carbon technologies, would result in an equally dramatic downturn in spending and employment as the onshore sector lost nearly all of its momentum.

It was a fall from grace plotted almost entirely by interests outside of Scotland, and ignored the arrival of onshore wind as the most reliable and cheapest of the renewable technologies on offer in the UK. The land-based wind sector remains largely in limbo to this day, awaiting a promised resurrection no less dramatic than that demanded by that droplet of water some 30 years ago.

That, however, is getting ahead of ourselves. For the purposes of this narrative, to begin the short, sharp history of Scottish onshore wind, it is time to meet Jeremy Sainsbury.

The assistant estate factor, one-time creator of a bespoke tweed to be worn while romping through the heather with an informal regiment of friends, knew that, as the 1980s wound to a close, the trio of small hydro projects under his management in Dumfries and Galloway could and should be generating more revenue, particularly in comparison with the mainstream technologies championed by large supply companies.

Output from the relatively small cascade, less than the equivalent of one modern wind turbine, had been designed to take advantage of measures included in the UK Energy Act 1983, created by the Conservative Government at Westminster in part to increase network access for private power generators. However the policy had failed to have the desired effect and, as plans for more substantial follow-on electricity market reform gathered momentum in the late 1980s, Sainsbury set his sights on tapping into revised measures.

Privatisation in Scotland took a separate path from the rest of Britain. The vertically integrated companies serving the nation, Scottish Power in the south and Scottish Hydro-Electric in the north, retained control over generation, networks and supply. Crucially, this included tariffs paid to independent generators, a situation perceived by some as distorting the market. 'Being trained as a chartered surveyor, and as a nosey little bugger, I began to take a closer look at the new legislation,' said Sainsbury.

His boss was keen to maximise the value of the natural resources at his disposal and was therefore supportive. The Forrest Estate near Kirkcudbright in Dumfries and Galloway has been owned by Norwegian industrial and property giant Fred Olsen Ltd, led by fourth-generation scion Fred Olsen, since 1952. Coniferous plantation forestry was the original mainstay with some 2,700 hectares established from 1953 to 1990 and, from 2001 to 2006, extended to the nearby Stranfasket property. Wood has been harvested up to three times, according to the estate, with the total sustainable production from clearfelling and thinning 'in excess of 20,000 tonnes per annum'. Making the most of the land, turning a profit from the hills and glens, was in the fabric of the place.

Olsen's younger brother Petter, helped by his mother Henriette, made the estate briefly newsworthy in 1984 when, as part of an extended battle over the family collection of paintings by Norwegian master Edvard Munch, they spirited away a collection of images including one version of iconic work *The Scream*. Fred had taken the artwork to Scotland in 1979 – squirreled away according to some, simply relocated according to others – but it was Petter's contention, later supported in court, that many of the paintings were rightfully his. The older brother nevertheless retained his own part of the Munch portfolio and eventually sold the majority of the collection in a $29.5 million deal in 2006. (Petter offloaded his version of *The Scream* for $120 million in 2012, just for the record.)

The episode can be read as typically Fred Olsen: a very private man who is polite but steadfast, ambitious yet practical, principled but pragmatic, willing to challenge the status quo. When it came time to addressing the less headline-grabbing matter of his Scottish estate's hydro portfolio, he was similarly disposed. Sainsbury remembers his Norwegian boss saying that if Westminster's Energy Act 1989 was not fit for the purposes of the estate, it should be challenged accordingly.

The legislation established supports for state-controlled nuclear power plants via the Non Fossil Fuels Obligation, known by its initials NFFO and pronounced by energy regulars and policy wonks as Noffo. The mechanism as originally designed imposed on once-nationalised suppliers a sort of carbon levy to help support the nuclear sector, which, unlike the rest of the electricity sector, would remain in state hands due to an overwhelming lack of private interest in the assets. As a by-product, the NFFO also offered supports for a limited number of alternative energy projects. The latter represented only a tiny percentage, roughly £100,000, of the around £1 billion per annum policy and, crucially for our story, only in England and Wales.

Ministers in London expected the minor element of the NFFO to encourage what the Department of Trade and Industry later described as:

> those renewable energy technologies that [were] approaching commercial competitiveness, by assisting their entry into the electricity generating market.

The lukewarm support for green power was part of a limited embrace of diversity in the supply market, upstart independent generators and increased efficiencies that formed part of a wider belief in the benefits of increased competition.

A senior civil servant, closely involved but like most mandarins faceless to the public (at least for the purposes of this narrative), said the non-nuclear NFFO measures were designed to build on an existing development and demonstration programme that itself had paved the way for construction of three wind farms in the pre-privatisation era, but in which the newly independent supply companies had 'zero interest; they didn't want to know'. The support mechanism – championed by 'green activists', enabled by 'willing and able' Whitehall players and approved by 'receptive ministers' – bypassed that market reluctance and some political opposition and kept European competition officials happy. 'Even in the early days, if you knew anything you knew renewable energy was inevitable,' said the civil servant.

Wind farms in the first years of the NFFO, at the earliest stage of commercialisation and located in Wales and south-west England, received average supports of between nine and 11 pence per kilowatt-hour, compared to the average UK electricity pool price over a similar period of 2.6 pence per kilowatt-hour. Bids in subsequent NFFO rounds, following a change to the terms of conditions designed to reduce market risk, dropped quickly to between three and six pence.

Scotland did not immediately adopt its own green power mechanism. According to Sainsbury this was, ironically in the case of the Forrest Estate, because the country already boasted a large and historic hydro-electric portfolio, controlled by the utilities, which lent its generation profile a greener and more diverse flavour than elsewhere in the UK. It was also because the electricity sector north of the border could produce far more power than it consumed, 10,000 megawatts compared with peak demand of 6,000 megawatts, with export potential limited by a relatively modest transmission connection between Scotland and points south. Sainsbury summed it up as 'no room at the inn' argument from existing energy sector interests. All of which, as the new age of energy policy dawned, appeared to leave the hydro trio on the Forrest Estate at a disadvantage when compared to renewable energy projects elsewhere in the UK.

Olsen and Sainsbury decided to test the case, the latter with action and the former with his chequebook. The estate joined forces with a number of other hydro projects in south-west Scotland and provocatively bid for a combined NFFO contract totalling nine megawatts, enough to power 10,000 homes. This was almost immediately ruled ineligible by regulators because it relied on export across the Scotland-England interconnector, judged by the watchdog as being against the rules. It nevertheless provided the proponents with something potentially more valuable: a piece of paper on which a legal case could be brought. The stakes quickly rose higher, via the intervention of an unexpected third party; generation interests in France were quietly eyeing the nuclear elements of the NFFO deal and were a hop, skip and jump, courtesy of a cross-Channel wire, from supplying the UK market under the same rules already being poked, probed and challenged from the kilted end of Britain.

The reader can draw their own conclusions about exactly what happened next, the whys and wherefores discussed, the type of language deployed behind closed doors.

The bottom line once the dust had settled was no change to NFFO rules for England and Wales, no backdoor for French suppliers, a bespoke contract for the troublesome Dumfries and Galloway hydro generators worth £53 per megawatt-hour running through 1999 and, most importantly, newfound momentum for a dedicated Scottish mechanism designed to offer newbuild green energy projects north of the border a route to market.

The Scottish Renewables Obligation, or SRO once boiled down, was variously described as a subsidy, a hand-out, a market intervention or a playing-field leveller, depending on ideology and feelings about the electricity market in general and renewables in particular. There were sections within the pre-devolution Scottish Office that considered it at worst a complete waste of time and money, and at best a distraction from the benefits of existing generation plant and in particular the promise of the nuclear sector.

Balancing that, however, and relishing their collective role as the pea under the St Andrews House mattress, was a small band of early movers in UK wind, armed with an almost religious faith in the technology, first-hand experience of pioneering projects in England and Wales and positive assumptions about the potential of the wind resource across Scotland. They kept up pressure on officials otherwise very reluctant to translate intention into action, and were prepared to move quickly to take advantage of the initial SRO bidding round when it was announced in the early 1990s.

One agitator was Ayrshire-born Stuart Hall, who held a degree in petroleum engineering and was a juggler and a member of Greenpeace and WWF. Despite the undergraduate training, 'I already knew oil was part of the problem and I wanted to be part of the solution,' he remembered. Following a period of globe-trotting, he enrolled in a one-year postgraduate Masters programme in resource and environmental engineering at the University of Salford in Manchester, England. The course included a field trip to the NFFO-supported Delabole wind farm near Camelford in Cornwall, which was the first commercial project in the UK when it was completed in 1991. Hall remembers the career-defining moment when confronted with the ten large-scale turbines executing electricity-producing cartwheels on the horizon: 'This is what I want to do,' he said to himself at the time.

In pursuit of that goal, the well-travelled Scot secured an unpaid summer work placement in mid-Wales with project development company Ecogen. The green energy specialist (the term 'renewables' was only starting to catch on across the sector) had its roots among veterans of the Centre for Alternative Technology in Powys and Cornwall Energy Project, including one Ted Leeming. The energetic, optimistic and committed Englishman was Hampshire-born, studied geography with communications and visual anthropology at degree level and, having travelled in similar mode to Hall, initially worked as a freelance photographer before become involved in energy in the early 1990s, specifically with a geothermal sector that never really managed lift-off. He was employed 'for the dole plus £10 and little more for several years. We never really got paid, it was amazing fun, with a great team of dedicated environmentalists working tirelessly for a common cause.'

A joint venture created by Ecogen, Japanese finance company Tomen and California wind farm specialist Seawest coordinated the commercial lift-off in Scotland. The partners, operating as Trigen, were successful in the second round of the English and Welsh auction mechanism and appeared to have a business model worth shouting about. It was well-placed to take advantage of the upcoming third round down south (NFFO-3) and newly minted first round in Scotland (SRO-1) and Stuart Hall was charged with returning to his native land, setting up an office – co-located within his flat on Maryhill Road, as it happens, in the shape of a single desk – and 'prospecting' for potential wind farm sites. Leeming would coordinate elements including planning and environmental, noise and bird surveys etc, once options were signed with landowners, with Hall being the boots on the ground in what was a very non-hierarchical structure.

The search for sites was low-tech in an almost *Blue Peter* kind of way but at the same time strategically inspired. The initial criteria was that any project would be outside of protected landscapes, easily accessible from the existing road system and near grid infrastructure. 'I followed the route of 33 kilovolt (power)lines, checked the Scottish Power seven-year statement (of network plans) for spare transformer capacity and then looked for a nearby hill,' said Hall. He worked from 1:50 Landranger Ordnance Survey maps highlighted with marker pens of different colours, a methodology that for future SRO rounds – and beyond – would extend to cover nearly the entirety of the Scottish mainland.

Ideal sites would in layman's terms be 'super windy', according to Hall, with average speeds of more than nine metres per second. 'I then started knocking on doors to try to find out who the landowner was,' he said. Lanarkshire farmer Willie Mitchell answered one of those approaches.

The landowner and businessman, who operated the family firm as Mitchell & Sons Ltd, was according to Hall 'on board right from the beginning' based mainly on an illustration of the potential returns. Mitchell had successfully purchased his land from the local estate after many generations of tenant farming and soon afterwards discovered a coal seam worth exploiting via opencast mining. The wind farm would be a logical addition as part of what was a very Scottish approach to getting the most from your natural resources. A signed exclusivity deal was followed by deployment of a ten-metre tall metal anemometry tower – a met mast in industry-speak – which was erected on the site by Hall (and some added muscle) and which would accurately characterise the wind profile. The computer chip on which relevant data was recorded had to be manually swapped out monthly; Hall became very familiar with the 90-minute journey south from Glasgow city centre to collect the relevant numbers.

Similar initiatives were taking place across other Ecogen sites in Scotland, in addition to investigations by rival developers. Windy Standard Limited, a joint venture between National Wind Power and, perhaps not surprisingly, one part of the Fred Olsen business empire, was eyeing a project on land managed by Jeremy Sainsbury in Dumfries and Galloway. Utility company Scottish Power was also starting to get interested; Robert McAlpine group spin-off Renewable Energy Systems and local outfit Energy Unlimited were similarly poised.

This was a small and tight-knit group of professionals, campaigners, academics and hobbyists centred largely in and around Glasgow, with tie-dye shirts often the uniform of choice; some participants helped to form Paisley community musical group Samba YaBamba, which remains active to this day. 'We worked hard but also had a lot of good parties, we used to all hang out together despite being competitors,' said Leeming. 'They were an amazing bunch of dedicated and honest people.'

There was a collective, communal spirit that extended to the wind farms themselves, typified by an early insistence by proponents such as Leeming and Hall that residents within a certain radius of any project should share in the benefits through annual set payments, a first in the UK. 'We were not corporations, we were still largely environmentally and community focused,' said Leeming. Benefits were 'not in the corporate ethos', he added but a precedent was established with those early SRO projects that became industry best practice and a key plank of the wind business' engagement with the people of Scotland over the next 20 years.

'Everybody who was working at that time thought of wind power as being a force for change,' said Hall. 'It is what they believed in, not just a job.'

The philosophy, and the future direction of wind, would be both refined and tested as the bidding deadline for the first round of the SRO approached. The era of commercial wind in Scotland was about to take off.

3

Pioneers

THE FIRST COMMERCIAL wind turbine in Scotland was completed in summer 1995 on Hagshaw Hill some 4km west of Douglas on land owned by Mitchell & Sons Ltd in the coalfields of South Lanarkshire. It was feeding clean, green power into the national grid by November and was one of 26 generators that would be erected and operational on the site by the year-end.

The B44/600 models travelled by ship from Denmark and were then transported by road to the project site off the A70. Components were fabricated by specialist company Bonus Energy, which had started life in 1980 as part of diversification efforts by agricultural irrigation system manufacturer Danregn. In 1981, the company built an initial turbine less powerful than John Brown's Costa Head pioneer from the 1950s but, by the mid-1990s, was one of the world's leading suppliers, offering machines more than ten times as powerful.

Construction crews at Hagshaw were mainly imported from England and Wales and had previous experience in building wind farms. Roads and other infrastructure were fabricated by DJ Construction of Colwyn Bay in Powys while electrical works were tackled by WT Parker, which was based in Grantham, Lincolnshire. Ecogen subsidiary Ocean Engineering managed the project on behalf of Trigen joint venture partners Tomen and Seawest.

'Mostly self-taught' engineer Jonathan Hill, now retired, supervised the design and procurement of electrical systems on behalf of the developer, following up with quality assurance management of construction and commissioning. He remembers a 'very tight work programme' but that the crews were happy on the job. 'They would work fairly long days but then would get a four-day weekend every fortnight. It was standard practice for them and they enjoyed it.' The project was finished ten days ahead of the original schedule.

Some of those involved at Hagshaw, including Hill, had previously built Trigen's St Breock wind farm near Wadebridge in Cornwall, which had been commissioned the previous year. Hill originally got involved with the industry in 1982 while working for the Northumbrian Energy Workshop in Hexham on small-scale and domestic installations as well as remote power supplies. The workshop would eventually spawn a number of groundbreaking wind energy companies responsible for, among other things, the first offshore wind farm in the UK at Blyth and a number of high-profile projects across the Inner and Outer Hebrides as well as Foula on Shetland.

Construction at the first Scottish commercial wind farm followed a pattern that has been refined at micro level over the decades but which in its most basic elements remains largely unchanged, some would even say unsophisticated. A quick summary may prove interesting to some readers; others will be forgiven the urge to skip ahead a few pages.

Crews first create an access off the existing public road network, with any necessary reinforcement of the local roads and bridges also carried out, before a central unpaved road is built into the wind farm site. A compound for portacabin offices and other amenities such as break rooms, toilets and parking will usually feature somewhere along the main entrance way. A series of smaller tracks are built to access the turbine locations, often a series of loops and spurs creating an organic swirl of infrastructure through the heather, moor or grasslands. The designs allow very large vehicles such as trailers and heavy-lift and telescopic mobile cranes to progress without taking sharp corners and, when things

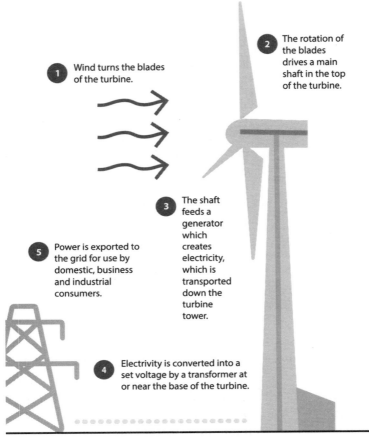

1. Wind turns the blades of the turbine.

2. The rotation of the blades drives a main shaft in the top of the turbine.

3. The shaft feeds a generator which creates electricity, which is transported down the turbine tower.

5. Power is exported to the grid for use by domestic, business and industrial consumers.

4. Electrivity is converted into a set voltage by a transformer at or near the base of the turbine.

How a wind turbine works.

go right, avoid stumbling into too-soft ground.

Each turbine location is separated from its neighbours by a few hundred metres and features a concrete foundation, either square or circular and metres deep, that is dug into the ground and reinforced throughout with steel rebar. Most of the substructure is reburied once complete, leaving a plinth above ground level to which the wind generator itself will be attached. Alongside each base is a 'hardstand' that will provide cranes with a solid and secure footing from which to lift generator components into the sky.

The turbines themselves consist of various elements, starting with a number of cylindrical steel tower sections, usually two or three, that are generally up to four metres in diameter and up to 30 metres long. The bottom section is secured either directly to the base or to a metal ring that is embedded in the concrete foundations. Multiple bolted connections are used in a pattern that is repeated between each of the subsequent tower segment. Cranes usually lift each piece into place, sometimes erecting the complete tower before progressing to the next location but, more recently, the practice has been to install all bottom units across the project before returning to complete the upper sections.

Most turbines include the electrical controls in the lower section of the turbine tower, with some also including the transformer which takes the raw power produced by the rotating blades and translates that electricity into a steady voltage for onward travel. Some projects also feature external transformers providing the same service.

At the top of each tower is the nacelle, again lifted into place during construction by a crane. This houses the generator, gearboxes if those feature, drivetrain, bearings and other elements necessary to translate wind into electricity. Nacelles are much bigger than they appear from the ground and more often than not feature enough space for crews to walk upright within the rectangular or circular shell; they often feature a hatch-like ceiling that allows for technicians to access and/or remove large-scale components through the roof via a crane. Some turbines, although rarely onshore, feature landing platforms at the top for access by helicopter.

Blades and the central rotor cap complete the picture. Wings tend to be made of fibreglass, are contoured and tapered to maximise efficiencies and are mainly but not always constructed as a single span rather than a number of bolted elements. At

Groundbreaking: the Hagshaw Hill wind farm near Douglas in South Lanarkshire became the first commercial project in Scotland when it entered operation in late 1995.
©Alan O'Dowd CC BY-SA-2.0, with kind permission

Hagshaw, the rotors were around 44 metres across but in modern onshore machines can be 150 metres and beyond. The swept area, ie the square metres covered as the three blades rotate around the horizontal axis, is one of the main elements governing how much power any one machine can produce. The size of aerofoils seems destined to increase further as the industry continues to innovate.

The rotor hub, also known as the nosecone or the cap, is along with the nacelle one of the most distinctive parts of any turbine. In a functional sense it secures the blades to the main structure and houses feathering and other control features. For wind geeks, it allows easy identification of various turbine types from a distance. Any child travelling across parts of Scotland or northern Europe will, if they are unlucky enough to have a parent either involved in or reporting on the wind industry, be familiar with the embarrassing shouts of 'Hey, those are Bonus, those ones are Vestas, the ones across the other side of the canal are older Siemens models' during long car journeys.

Completing the wind farm picture is electrical infrastructure: underground cables link either strings or loops of turbines to a central substation, where the power is gathered, stepped up to a higher voltage and delivered to the national grid network for distribution to consumers and businesses. Hagshaw itself is technically two wind farms, since SRO-1 contracts were limited to a particular size, and so its substation effectively knits the two separate electrical entities into one point of export.

Hagshaw's total output was 15.6 megawatts and, weighted on the basis of anticipated annual output, it was part of 46 megawatts of capacity contracted in the first SRO round. Bids averaged four pence per kilowatt-hour and payments would be linked to inflation for a 15-year period. In terms of success in the auction, it all came down to understanding how much electricity the project would be capable of producing, how much it would cost to get there and what your rivals were likely to bid. For Trigen, US company Seawest was particularly enamoured of the bottom line, according to Jonathan Hill, rather than wider issues of innovation or, in and of itself, green generation. 'The Americans were looking to get every penny out of the project. Will that add commercial value, they would ask. If not, the answer was always no.'

Design of Hagshaw was an 'iterative' process, according to Stuart Hall, and at the very outset was subject to what he described as 'the hippie element' well represented in wind power at the time. 'One person in the Wales office said turbines should be arranged in a circle. "Like standing stones," she told me, "That would be quite nice."' Potential layout patterns were instead tested against one constraint, for instance potential bird impacts, and then revised before moving onto the next parameter. In that way ornithology, hydrology, noise, landscape and potential power profiles, among other items,

MYTH 2

Wind power is noisy

There were certainly some noisy machines in the early years of the wind industry, and faulty hardware can still cause a problem, but huge progress has been made in this area. Generally speaking, modern wind farms produce less than 40 decibels at distances of 400 metres, well below the level of background noise in most communities. Low frequency sounds known as amplitude modulation are also produced by some but not all wind farms, and international standards are currently being developed to better understand and address this issue.

were eventually reflected in an ever-evolving design.

Ted Leeming remembered his budget for a planning application in the early days, including full environmental impact statement, being capped at £27,750. The equivalent for a modern wind farm can be up to £1 million.

When the completed planning application for Hagshaw arrived in early 1994 for determination by local authority Clydesdale District Council, 'nobody had heard of wind farms,' remembers Stuart Hall. 'We had to educate everybody as we went, all the councillors and the officers.' Some concerns were raised by local pigeon enthusiasts who were convinced the machines would interfere with homing instinct; those fears were eventually allayed by sometime wind industry *bête noire* RSPB. One elected member of the council felt the machines at 60 metres would be too high, which resulted in a reduction of overall tip heights, ie the distance between the ground and the end of a turbine blade at its highest point, to 55 metres.

The Scottish Office was also in unfamiliar territory; the government paperwork necessary to allow payments under the SRO lagged behind generation at Hagshaw by around six months, which meant that official offtake company Scottish Power paid 1.4 pence per kilowatt-hour for output during the interim period. There were some grumblings about the rights and wrongs of the situation but actual legal wrangling was avoided when, in summer 1996, the utility company struck a deal to buy the wind farm. A press officer for Scottish Power told *The Glasgow Herald* at the time, in the sort of remarks sadly no longer encouraged among comms across the industry:

> The fact that we have bought the wind farm from Trigen means that particular dispute is finished. The £15 million price we paid takes in everything and covers all eventualities. Now they have got the money and we have got the wind farm. Everybody is happy.

Other projects soon followed behind, in Dumfries and Galloway, Argyll and Bute and the Highlands. The footprint would spread to the Borders, Shetland and Orkney. When the SRO regime was wound down in the late 1990s after three rounds, 150 megawatts of capacity had been awarded (although not all of those were built).

What did that additional generation mean, in terms of day-to-day life? Purely in terms of power produced, not a huge amount. In the most basic terms, the 15.6 megawatts installed at Hagshaw Hill can at full capacity provide less than one per cent of Scotland's electricity demand, around 10,000 houses, but of course it cannot do that all of the time.

Like a car engine with a certain horsepower, the nameplate capacity at any wind farm is only an indication of what is possible rather than what will always be the case. Turbines in Scotland, as a rule of thumb, produce some degree of power to the grid at least 80 per cent of the time and, depending on site specifics, hit between 30 per cent and 50 per cent of full capacity over the span of any given year. To extend the automotive analogy, the standard 'wind power' car sits in the garage inactive for up to 20 per cent of the time but is travelling on the road at various speeds (up to the full nameplate horsepower) for the remainder of its life. Those living on what are essentially resource motorways – windy spots – hit top speed more often, those on the breeze back roads are a bit less road-tested. The bottom line is that Hagshaw on average produces a very tiny slice of Scotland's power each year.

However, as the champions of the sector will point out, it is crucial to remember two distinct facts about wind energy. First, unlike traditional power-generation, it effectively and quite magically requires zero direct fuel to create the power. Returning to the car metaphor, you essentially drive out of the showroom with your shiny new automobile and, although you had to pay for it and will need to cover insurance and maintenance etc, you will never have to fill up the tank for as long as you own it; instead, it will be 'fuelled' by the wind. This simple but remarkable element is often overlooked, somewhat unbelievably, when discussing the wider pros and cons, options and policies surrounding the technology.

The second feature of onshore wind power to keep in mind, according to energy experts, is that it is a dispersed resource so cannot be judged by the output of just one site. To introduce another analogy, traditional generation is very much like that of a supercomputer, in which all the processing takes place in one location via a gigantic machine (with flashing lights and spinning discs etc, if that helps to visualise). However, wind energy is more akin to 'hive mind' computing in which the power of a thousand smart phones is harnessed via a network to produce the same processing ability as a supercomputer, but from a huge variety of locations. Even when one part of this network is down (power outage, lack of wind), another is up and running and ready to provide what is necessary to get the job done. Again, this wider picture tends to be lost when discussions on wind get heated as they inevitably do.

Hagshaw was an indisputable pioneer even if some, depending on disposition, would consider it the thin end of an unsavoury wedge; it was the first of a new class of generation in Scotland which over a period of 20 years grew large enough, when the wind is strong, to meet both the country's entire electricity demand and to export excess power to other parts of the UK. Over the most recent full-year period, the renewable segment, made up mainly of onshore wind, met more than 50 per cent of gross electricity consumption north of the border, according to government figures, and outpaced all other rivals including nuclear and fossil fuels.

In the late 1990s, that was all in the future, however, and there was change on the horizon. Hagshaw and a number of other early projects had turbines producing electricity for consumers and had proved that wind was a realistic generation option but the SRO auction rounds that facilitated the initial growth were coming to an end and there was a new politics taking hold. New Labour under Tony Blair had come to power across the UK, Scotland was preparing to re-establish its own Parliament in Edinburgh following the 1997 devolution vote and global targets for tackling climate change had been adopted under the UN Kyoto Protocol.

Wind was a decidedly minor player but had established a toehold in the Scottish energy sector and, with those carbon reduction targets to the fore, was being encouraged to spread its wings via a shiny new government support mechanism that would be introduced at Westminster and embraced by Holyrood.

With the arrival of the new Renewables Obligation mechanism, due to kick off in 2002, the hippies, the activists and the dreamers would surpass even their grandest expectations; their collective outlook and championed technology spreading well beyond the green fringe and into the mainstream.

Some wind devotees were even buying suits as the new decade got underway; exponential growth, big business and serious money were about to take centre stage.

4

Entering the Mainstream

THE NEWLY ESTABLISHED Scottish wind sector would expand 40-fold between 2002 and 2018 on the back of UK government measures designed specifically to ramp up deployment and cut carbon emissions.

As an instrument of policy, the Renewables Obligation support mechanism, or RO as it quickly became known, was relatively straightforward. A 2001 preview of the legislation, produced by the Parliamentary Office of Science and Technology as POST Note 164, provided a handy synopsis:

> The RO requires all licensed electricity supplies to obtain an increasing proportion of electricity from eligible renewable sources.

The exact details of how it would work were of course fiendishly complicated and massively bureaucratic but the two main planks of the RO – the requirement for suppliers to generate their own or buy third-party green power, and in increasing amounts over time, via a certificate system – set the stage for an explosion in onshore wind deployments.

'After Labour came in, the industry essentially went into limbo while they were developing the RO,' said Ted Leeming, who together with Stuart Hall had by this time formed independent company Natural Power to take forward wind projects. 'Give Tony Blair his due. If it wasn't for him, renewables would not be where it is today. It take my hat off to him for being brave and putting in place the policies for getting the entire industry off the ground.'

The new mechanism, at is most basic and without getting distracted by the terms and conditions, offered a route to market for any project that could connect to the grid, and at a fixed premium on top of the wholesale price of electricity. Those payments eventually nearly doubled the money earned from each megawatt-hour produced.

Parts of Whitehall, which had been working on a follow-up to the bid-based NFFO/SRO mechanism when New Labour was elected, were not very keen. Our civil servant from the previous chapter called the policy 'a retrograde step' that would be 'hideously expensive' because it failed to provide any real incentive for cost reductions over time. He retired soon after.

The devolved government in Edinburgh, a still-young Labour and Liberal Democrat coalition supported by many of the old Scottish Office backroom staff, would be in charge of drawing up the legislation as it applied north of the border. It would be known (inevitably) as the Renewables Obligation Scotland, or ROS, and would both dovetail and be interchangeable with British efforts to ramp up green electricity from a very low level to ten per cent by 2010 (Northern Ireland would be treated separately under what would eventually become the all-island single electricity market).

UK ministers were obliged to facilitate that massive growth in green generation after signing the Kyoto protocol along with 192 other countries in 1997. The goal was to address global warming by slowing the growth rate of greenhouse gases in the atmosphere. Emissions would be kept to a level that would 'prevent dangerous anthropogenic interference with the climate system', according to the terms of the protocol. It almost seems quaint, looking back.

The UK quota of ten per cent was specifically defined and so codified in the EU Directive on Electricity Production From Renewable Energy Sources 2001, designed to bring member states in line with the aims of Kyoto. Baseline surveys in 1997 found the Britain lagged well behind most European countries in terms of renewable electricity, with only Belgium faring worse in percentage terms.

Ray Hunter, who at the start of the RO era was head of development in Scotland for Renewable Energy Systems, said the new mechanism was designed to meet the 'significant challenge' of the 2010 target by letting industry know 'we want projects to be built with minimal impediment'. The old auction regime, he added, had been more about 'producing power at incremental competitive costs', which while a fine goal in itself produced an unintentional drag on newbuild projects that would if retained have worked against the EU goals.

Hunter knows what he is talking about. He earned a first class Honours degree in engineering science at Aberdeen University and, despite relocating to the Central Belt in the late 1970s, still supports Aberdeen FC; 'the resurgent Aberdeen FC', he would probably say.

His renewables career initially focused on wave energy conversion at government agency National Engineering Laboratory (NEL). It took a sideways step after five years via the NEL's newly-formed test facility the National Wind Turbine Centre outside Glasgow. He spearheaded development efforts in Scotland for Renewable Energy Systems starting in 1998 and secured a number of wind farm contracts under the SRO, although not all of those projects were built as originally planned.

The latter was indicative of one of the main problems with the auction mechanism as established by the NFFO; for most developers, the certainty of a government-backed contract was necessary before rolling the dice with a planning application, particularly in the early days when the deliberations of local authority officials and councillors were often winding and protracted, with sometimes random outcomes. There were no guarantees, which meant boards were simply unwilling to risk the considerable upfront spending necessary to get a project to the stage where construction could begin without a contract.

Unfortunately, the converse was also true: there was no guarantee that projects securing market capacity under the SRO would make it across the hurdle of planning, since they generally waited until after the auction to start the process. Uncertainty ruled.

Hunter described the staggered auction system of NFFO/SRO as an additional problem; developers were squeezed into an artificial timeline in which periods of intense activity were layered with sometimes extended downtimes. Between the stop/start and the failure rate of the auction winners, the young industry struggled to create any momentum.

The pending RO regime was designed to offer relief on all fronts, and at least north of the border was part of a meeting of minds across multiple interests. In the period before the new mechanisms came into being, Hunter remembers, suppliers, developers, generators, stakeholders and government were all combining to pull in the same direction and in the national interest.

'We were all in the same room sitting down and trying to decide how best to do wind,' he said. 'It was all about what we could do for the country.'

He contrasted the mood with that in England, where an 'antagonistic' approach was already developing between the industry and local authorities, residents and consultees. 'In Scotland, communities were not seen as the opposition, wind was seen as a natural change in the countryside. We got through the SRO without wind being seen as a negative; down south, it was already a pariah. It meant development was usually a 'when' for us; down south, it was an 'if'. A lot of that had to do with the Scottish government approach.'

With the general philosophy of the RO agreed, the SRO experience under the collective industry belt, and broad agreement among energy players about the positives ahead, the Scottish government commissioned renewables consultancy Garrad Hassan to quantify the opportunity at hand. In the relatively constrained language of consultancy-speak the report, entitled 'Scotland's Renewable Resource 2001', outlined the significant size of the prize for Scotland:

> RO certificates... will be tradable between all suppliers in Great Britain. This means in effect that the location of renewable energy plant is not tied to the demand. This has led to speculation that, given its rich renewable resources, Scotland may be a natural exporter... to England and Wales.

Hunter summarised:

> Scotland saw an opportunity. It could create for itself separate renewables targets that would help the UK, and Westminster was happy for Scotland to do that. Go ahead and build what you can, they said.

The Garrad Hassan study ignored potential projects in urban clusters, designated protected landscapes, RAF low-flying zones and areas deemed to be topographically difficult, ie too steep. It also dismissed inland waters, perhaps to protect famous monsters (or giant eels), in apparent reply to what must have been a suggestion from some since-forgotten quarter: 'It would be pointlessly expensive to site onshore wind farms on lochs,' wrote Garrad Hassan drily.

Factors not considered in the assessment, even though subsequently proven to be important in the distribution of wind projects, included radar interference, protected species, buffer zones and wild land areas.

The report considered a variety of renewables but put extra effort into the potential of land-based turbines, largely because it was already a proven entity. 'In view of its near-term importance in meeting government targets, and the increasing amount of development activity in Scotland, onshore wind has been examined in more detail than any of the other technologies.' At a cost cut-off of seven pence per kilowatt-hour, lower than what was eventually secured during the RO regime, Garrad Hassan estimated roughly 11,500 megawatts of available resource, roughly equal to Scotland's entire generation fleet at that time. Around half of the total identified wind resource was said to be developable at less than three pence per kilowatt-hour of generation cost.

To the end of tapping those reserves, the Renewables Obligation (Scotland) Order 2002 came into force on 1 April 2002. Environment Minister Ross Finnie of the Liberal Democrats said while shepherding the legislation through the Holyrood Parliament: 'We have gone through much consultation with the industry, trying to get the detail right.'

The minister was confident the order would enable Scotland to deliver an initial renewable electricity target of 18 per cent for 2010, well above the UK-wide level, and 'contribute an additional reduction of 2.5 million tonnes of carbon a year to help the UK meet its Kyoto target'. Finnie told MSPs:

We hope the RO will stimulate the development of a new and thriving industry in Scotland, foster innovation, bring new technologies such as wave energy to the market, and provide a solid foundation for delivering further progress in the field of renewables.

The starting gun had been fired on a what would in short order become party time for Scotland's wind industry.

New applications almost immediately went into overdrive and the collective planning process was at times severely strained. By early 2003, some 120 projects were already working their way through some stage of consideration either at local or national level and what was considered by some as a development goldrush was beginning to take shape as companies bundled in to take advantage of the opportunities on offer.

Agents, following more systematically in the footsteps of Stuart Hall's pioneering approach, knocked on doors across the country, particularly if a hill was nearby. Hundreds or even thousands of land options were signed in the course of a few years with an eye to potential development of wind farms; met masts were erected, negotiations advanced, deals done.

In-trays groaned across local authority planning departments, particularly in those areas with high ground and existing grid infrastructure. Councils were largely left to develop their own strategies for dealing with the rush: some like Perth and Kinross took the decision that wind was unwelcome, some opened dialogue with developers to steer projects in a particular direction or geography, some maintained a decidedly ad hoc approach.

Highland Council, with a wind-rich and sparsely-populated land mass the size of Belgium, was already popular with developers from the SRO days and so more experienced than most with the sector. That was just as well, given the number of projects queueing at the door of the planning department; its subsequent experience is both illustrative and illuminating.

Area planning manager David Mudie was raised in Alloa and studied at both Napier and Heriot-Watt Universities in Edinburgh, working as a building engineer before moving into the planning sphere with the capital's city council in 2000.

He possesses a nuanced and rounded view of the wind journey in Scotland, having joined Highland in 2004 to take his place at the coalface of RO development. He can laugh about the crazy years but shies away from hyperbole; there were lessons to be learned and, for Highland, something to be achieved in terms of an economic catalyst and carbon reduction. The local authority, after all, took a dramatically different approach to the wind sector than many other councils: projects would bring benefits to local communities and a new string to the bow of the regional economy. It was a sector worth encouraging, within the usual limits, and policies were drawn up to that effect.

The subsequent work done by the planners, often blazing new assessment trails into unknown development territory, was 'highly regarded' not only by stakeholders public and private, but also by industry and by the Edinburgh government.

Highland Council in the early years of the wind boom accepted applications at local level but these were more often than not passed up the food chain to planners in the Inverness HQ. Projects were assessed against a Government-issued Planning Advice Note and non-statutory guidance until the Highland Structure Plan was put in place in the early 2000s.

Projects became more complicated over time, with bigger footprints and larger machines and more frequently planned within or adjacent to higher value landscapes. The council developed an in-house standard for assessing potential visual impacts which remains head and shoulders above rivals, according to Mudie.

From 2008, the local authority was tackling an average of eight to ten new major wind farm applications each year with three planning officers devoted full-time to the sector. Between 2012 and 2015, the rate spiked with a total of 55 proposals lodged in Highland.

As an indication of the level of spending required to prepare the hundreds of wind farm applications for determination across the 32 local authorities of Scotland, each project assessment was estimated to cost around £25,000 in development management and councillor time, not including contributions from other parts of the public sector. Any appeal, which was almost inevitable following a rejection, would push the costs even higher.

Reactions to wind farms were often polarised dramatically between those with an interest in the project – be that landowner, developer, estate worker – and those who would view it from the outside such as residents, tourists, special interests. There were also anti movements both local and national, organised and fringe, but more on those in Chapter Seven.

Larger projects of 50 megawatts and above, generally anything bigger than 20 to 25 turbines, were determined by Scottish ministers but still required the input of local councils as statutory consultees. Across the system as a whole some obvious mistakes were made – either with what was approved or what was denied, depending on who you ask – but broadly speaking the end result largely balanced the demands of development with protections for the environment.

Across the Highland Council area, Mudie can only point to a handful of wind farms, often consented by Scottish government officials on appeal or by Edinburgh ministers in the case of very large wind farms, where the negative impacts outweigh the good. He warned, however, that there remains the risk of going too far.

Scotland as a whole is potentially sacrificing the quality of landscapes in a rush to reduce our carbon footprint. We can of course achieve both, but we won't know if we've gone too far until it is too late to go back.

The sheer number of projects emerging successfully from the planning process, and the guaranteed route to market during the RO years, combined to offer a tantalising prospect for established wind industry supply chain players from around the world. For Danish man Claus Poulsen, who set up a sales office in Manchester for German turbine manufacturer Nordex just as the RO era was starting, business skyrocketed.

'We had 100 per cent growth within two months,' he joked when asked, 'going from one to two employees.' It was typically self-deprecating humour from the affable Dane that pointed towards a wider truth: staff numbers rose quickly as operations expanded at a significant rate, to around 30 in the short term and then to between 70 and 80, all within a period of four years.

MYTH 3

Wind power makes you sick

No medically accepted evidence has been found linking wind turbines with illness in nearby residents, sometimes known as wind turbine syndrome. In fact, research from Australia reports a high correlation between those reporting such effects and media coverage of the syndrome, rather than the presence or otherwise of wind farms. It appears to be a disease that only those philosophically opposed to wind power can catch, however sincerely felt.

Nordex in the early 2000s was flush with investment funds following a successful public flotation and had been actively eyeing export markets. Long distance sales efforts over hollow-sounding landline phones 'had not been much of a success' and rivals had already established a physical foothold in the UK market which, according to Poulsen, meant boots on the ground would be necessary.

'A few old colleagues were based in Manchester and recommended the quality of life, so no real science in the selection,' he remembered. 'It [the new office] was between the wind farms in Scotland and the north of England, and a lot of the developers and finance people in the south and London, so it worked.'

Poulsen, originally from the port city of Esbjerg on the west coast of Denmark, had started life in the shipping sector before attending business school at age 29. He completed his studies as the wind business was making waves in his home country, with four world-leading companies based within a few hours of his home town.

He joined Nordex, which despite its German headquarters had roots and ownership interests in Denmark, and within a year he was on his way to Manchester. 'There was strong market interest in the UK in what we were offering,' he said, with obvious belief in the product he was preparing to send into a growing market.

An initial Scottish deal was signed with Powergen, later to be called E.ON, for the Bowbeat project in the Borders. A total of 24 turbines would be built at the Moorfoot Hills site with operations beginning in 2002 and running through to the present time. 'It was scary,' said Poulsen of landing the first big deal. 'I joined this industry with a non-technical background, I remember thinking, shit, what are we to do now? From there it was about focus and building information and understanding what you are trying to sell.'

He and his growing team secured 'a lot of projects' and, in hindsight, he allowed that 'there may have been times when we took on too much'.

The rewards, however, were significant. 'When things were peaking, I remember there were times when almost everybody was sold out,' said Poulsen. 'Due to the market dynamics, the margins were way higher than they are today. That's how it was for a number of years.'

Poulsen left the UK around the end of 2010 to pursue other challenges both within wind and in other industries, but regularly travels back to Scotland on business and often gets a chance to see his handiwork from the air. 'They will always be those landmarks out the window as I fly into Edinburgh. That's great.'

It was a journey replicated many times over: developers local, national and international opened offices in the Central Belt before branching out into more ignored parts of Scotland; established civil engineering companies expanded workforces by 100, 200, 300 per cent; rival heavy works outfits from England and Ireland set up shop; myriad consultancies with a range of services offerings popped up in every corner of the country. There were operations and maintenance contractors, service hubs, suppliers of spare parts, transport specialists. There were bird watchers and newt counters and badger mappers and photographers, there were outdoor access specialists and security guards. Men and women were broadly represented at all levels, which shouldn't have to be acknowledged but was nevertheless in stark contrast to the still very much male-dominated landscape of the power sector at the time.

There was plenty of opportunity and it spread across all of those already involved in wind and those who wanted to be involved in wind; and all because the RO projects were legion.

The total installed turbine fleet across the country rose from less than 200 megawatts in the wake of the SRO years to nearly 8,000 megawatts when the phased closure of the support mechanism was finally completed and the final stragglers were accredited by Ofgem in 2018–19. If you assume (unscientifically, but probably not far off the mark) an average project size of 30 to 40 megawatts, that is more than 200 separate wind farms.

Up close and personal: the wind sector regularly opened its doors to the public as it sought to engage with the curious, the undecided and the opposed.
© Todd Westbrook

Build totals in Scotland started slowly as RO projects wound their way through the planning system, financial close was secured, contractors lined up and construction timetables established. A total of 159 megawatts went live in 2004 – just two years into the new mechanism – with 200 megawatts following in 2005; construction ramped up quickly with more than 500 megawatts going live in 2009 and nearly 900 megawatts in 2012. A record 1,320 megawatts was completed by developers rushing to accredit projects as the RO clock began to click towards the end date in 2017, with 350 megawatts completing in 2018 to bring down the curtain on a period of momentous change.

Wind as an asset class grew by the equivalent of one new utility-scale gas-fired power station each and every year under the RO mechanism. Projects were built in nearly all local authority areas: north and south, east and west, rural and less-so, and on the islands. Higher ground was favoured where possible but, given Scotland's wind profile, it would be an exaggeration to say that every array straddled a hilltop.

What did all those megawatts look like on the ground? What did the establishment of a new industry, of that wind fleet, involve?

Initially, and in time lapse imagery across the RO years, it was about a swarm of logistics. Ports on all of Scotland's coasts took deliveries, from either end of the Central Belt to the north-east, west coast and islands. Ocean-going vessels both adapted and bespoke unloaded industrial-scale components onto quaysides sometimes thronged with competing interests and at other times as the sole customer, for storage or immediate dispatch, atop specialist transport lorries. Turbines travelled by motorways, A, B, C and unclassified roads to wind farm sites on brownfields, agricultural acreage, among plantation forestry and across upland plateaus and grouse moors. Picture an army of stevedores, crane operators, drivers and police escorts at work; follow the routes as the first few journeys snake inland before becoming an established migration pattern.

Next came the mud – many, many hundreds of hectares of the gluey, suction-inducing, shite-brown Scottish variety across the 20-year lifespan of the industry. Construction is by its nature a dirty, disruptive business and while a finished wind farm can be a sort of kinetic energy-producing sculpture park, the interim across the rain-lashed fringes of north-west Europe was a tangle of earth-spackled bulldozers, dump trucks, excavators, scrapers and telescopic cranes. And lots of that mud. There were steam rollers, concrete mixers, telescopic cranes and backhoes. At some points during the RO boom, there was not a spare civil engineering vehicle to be found in Scotland. There were flashing warning lights and beeping reverse sirens at every turn. A workforce bloomed: hundreds and thousands of men and women in well-worn hard hats, faded high-vis clothing and steel-toed boots. Visiting executives made special trips to far-off concerns wearing just-issued PPE bedecked with company logos; strategy became action, blueprint projects became reality, theory became practice.

A million journeys were saved as stone for use in wind farms was pulled from hundreds of temporary on-site quarries called borrow pits. Packed quadrilaterals of conifers planted a half century ago were felled in every corner of the country, harvested and the remains chewed into splintered pieces left to become increasingly less verdant with each passing week, designed to degrade back into the landscape more quickly than the tangle of clear cut on a neighbouring hillside. No man's land comparisons did not usually last for very long.

Across the country, thousands of holes were dug, miles of rebar wrestled into place, millions of tonnes of cement poured. Heavy, specialist lifting equipment inched onto and across sites, many awkward beetles among the anthills of activity, more often than not lumbering into the Scotland landscape from Denmark, Germany and Ireland. Drivers spent their money, shared their culture, mingled with the locals. Methodologies were refined, experiences multiplied, lessons learned. Turbines were erected, a word that loses its sophomoric guffaw factor once repeated for the thousandth time. Winds were fought across a 20-year timeline, ropes deployed, human limits tested against the most benign and challenging of weather conditions, and that was during the summers. Work often struggled through early snows and long, bitter upland winters.

An increasing brigade of mountain-ready engineers and technicians, kitted out with harnesses, carabiners, climbing helmets and high-altitude smiles, laboured a hundred metres into the air bringing life to an inanimate collection of hardware. One by one, thousands of generators were commissioned, three times as many blades began to turn, coils were enticed to produce power. Electricity was created.

Wires to carry the collected production of this new industry, the output of a different kind of economy, were buried beneath the ground, hung on wooden poles, stretched across roads and into substations carved in neat rectangles into forests, farmland and waste ground. More substantial cables travelled to meet the lattice towers marching toward market as part of the expanding national grid network. Control centres were established, fresh faces sat in front of screens and interfaces fed by data links from hundreds of miles distant, conditions were relayed, adjustments made, service crews dispatched when things went wrong or optimisation was required.

A dictionary's worth of project names reflects the spread across all of Scotland's regions and evokes landscapes from Lowland to Highland, island to coast, moorland to upland, farm to city: Novar, Hoprigshiels, Clyde, An Suidhe, Pearie Law, Milton of Fishrie, A'Chruach, Spurness, Mossmorran, Beinn Ghrideag, Wathegar, Lochluichart, Beinn an Tuirc, St Johns Hill, Cathkin Braes, Calliachar, Berry Burn, Little Raith and hundreds more. The stumbles of the SRO years were left in the rear-view. A new sector was established and sustained. Clean, green, exciting.

Other parts of the power generation market, meanwhile, went into reverse. The 240-megawatt Chapelcross nuclear power plant in Dumfries and Galloway was decommissioned in 2004 while the coal-fired plants at Cockenzie in East Lothian (1,200 megawatts) and Longannet in Fife (2,400 megawatts) were shut down in 2013 and 2016, respectively. The greenhouse gas intensity of the electricity sector in Scotland fell to 54 grams per kilowatt-hour in 2016 from 320 grams per kilowatt-hour as recently as 2010. The country has already, and in the very near future will regularly, produce more electricity from renewable energy than it consumes.

There were updates and refinements to the RO after the original legislation was introduced and targets were regularly increased both at Scottish and UK level, albeit with the former always well ahead of the latter. Ever-increasing ambitions for green electricity marched arm and arm with the never-ending appetite showed by development companies and utilities for more wind farms; the experience on the ground was equal parts exhilarating and chaotic.

For project owners, the prices to be paid for supply of turbines, construction contracts, grid charges and all the other elements that went into the costs column were outweighed by what was on offer in terms of profit. Some called the RO a licence to print money with rates of return that were much, much higher than those possible under the old SRO. The focus on increased deployment, the necessary focus on increased deployment, in emission terms, dictated that one of the key elements of any prudent public spending exercise was all but abandoned:

'The downward costs trajectory of the SRO didn't continue,' said Ray Hunter. 'The system simply did not incentivise savings.'

The returns on offer soon started to attract attention from many outside the traditional renewables community; in the heart of the RO era this took the form of what was often labelled 'city money'. It was not a term of affection, and according to some in the industry it helped to establish a wind farm feeding frenzy in Scotland that at times encouraged bad projects and indirectly hastened a coming storm.

'The money fuelled speculation and some inappropriate, crazy development,' said Hunter disapprovingly.

Exactly how much money, and whether that was offset by the jobs, economic benefit, system change and carbon reductions on offer, became the central debate of the wind sector as the new decade bedded in and politicians began to question the very basis of the RO.

First Intermission

REPORTING ON SCOTTISH renewables in the early RO years was largely a chronicle of aspiration, confidence and anticipation. This was going to be big, it was going to transform the country; hell, it was going to change the world and along the way it was going to make everybody rich. At first there was not much happening in terms of boots on the ground but by God the planning for the assault was detailed and ambitious. The forces of opposition – fossil fuels, nuclear, nimbys, foot-dragging politicians – were going to be blown away.

The byword at the start was enthusiasm. Everyone involved wanted to talk about what they were doing, about their plans for success, about the grand vision behind that first wind farm, that first contract, that first application. Interviews were candid affairs fuelled in part by unbridled optimism; more often than not my telephone call or face-to-face sitdown would be the first time anyone outside the wind industry itself had been interested in what they were doing. Yes, there was a dedicated press that dealt with renewables but in large part this ignored Scotland and was in any case focused on policies more than projects. And the latter was where all the action was; theory was fine, actually creating electrons from the passing breeze was far more fulfilling.

I got involved almost by accident. The gig started as a one-day a week string intended to provide a base layer of income to support a broad-based freelance career in the mainstream press. My résumé wasn't too bad at the time and I had made a decent living in four countries across two continents. Experiences included daily regional newspapers, national Sundays, magazines, freelance features, regular columns, wire services. It was the pre-internet age, but some of those early efforts – sometimes okay, sometimes cringeworthy – can still be found in retrospectively stocked, usually ignored and always fusty archives of the web.

Freelancing from a Highland base proved difficult, however, for a mid-career hack without much experience in the UK. I had moved to Scotland, the country of my wife's birth – a place that I had called home on and off through parts of the late 1980s and early 1990s and where we opted to lay down well-travelled roots and raise our expanding family. We'd bought a house – self-certified mortgage, remember those? – managed to get pregnant (again) and there were bills to pay.

I made those tentative first queries about wind farms just as the sector was starting to take off and suddenly an opportunity presented itself. Renewables in Scotland seemingly had no one to tell its story so it was natural that calls were taken, information offered without spin or filter, opinions put forward. The publication I represented was fiercely independent, we reported success and failures, highs and lows, milestones and mishaps. We became a must-read for anyone involved in the wind industry, big and small, new and old, public and private, even when we wrote things that the business did not particularly want to see in black and white.

The approach outweighed my own natural scepticism about the narrow confines of industry reporting, about what some labelled (incorrectly) trade journalism.

The latter found our independence arrogant: 'You'll never get advertisers,' they lectured, 'nobody pays to be regularly hauled over the coals.' The publication was also held in contempt by the so-called mainstream press, even though we beat them to story after story of national importance, and were robbed blind when they picked up our exclusives without credit and ran them as their own. 'The subs stripped it out,' was the usual cry about attribution. A story we broke, although not one of mine, even featured as part of a page three spread in *The Sun*. No credit, again, but, hey, talk about a claim to fame.

In the end, the string somehow morphed into a full-time job and a steady progression up the editorial tree. For much of the time, particularly in the early days, it was an absolute ball.

5

Money, Jobs, Land and Subsidies

SOMETIME IN THE late 2000s, probably around an oilclothed table in a kitchen with a view out over the rolling agricultural landscape of the north-east of Scotland, a landowner sat down with a developer to discuss the potential for a wind farm in Aberdeenshire.

The gentleman farmer was worried about the risks involved in installing a turbine array and whether the hassles of planning and construction, and potentially annoying the neighbours, would be worth the eventual returns.

'How's your marriage?' interrupted the developer.

The estate owner was taken aback by the odd question. 'What does my marriage have to do with it?' he replied.

'If you have any doubts, deal with those now,' said the wind man while passing over a one-sheet illustrative business case. 'After your wife sees how much money this brings in, she'll be with you forever.'

This reply – in what might admittedly be an apocryphal tale – was a clincher, even if a bit old school in terms of its gender politics. And as the RO era took root, it was often the one-word business case of 'money' that turned an increasing number of heads: returns calculated in the millions permeated the industry.

'There were times during the conversations in the late 2000s when you would suddenly see there was a lot of cash in the game,' said one contractor active during the boom years. She added: 'The power price including the RO certificate was around £100 per megawatt-hour during much of this period. In other parts of Europe, people were building projects at prices half that level; the UK returns were significantly better.'

When discussing money, there is really no such thing as a 'typical' wind farm in Scotland; variables such as wind resource, grid costs, environmental and other constraints, transport requirements and a myriad of other elements combine to create a series of largely bespoke projects, each with its own challenges and therefore its own financial profile. Complicating any broadbrush conclusions are wind farm developers and suppliers, which are very reluctant to share exact details of specific projects, while portfolio effects, shared costs and other paperwork shenanigans – all legal, of course – further muddy the comparability across actual accounts from many a real-life installation.

For illustrative purposes, and to keep the litigious at bay, we will therefore consider the financial side of wind by building a generic project, which we will call Scotia, located in a middle-of-the-road wind regime (for Scotland) in a bog-standard local authority and featuring widely-available technologies and a comparatively normal grid connection. We have magicked away at-risk species, radar problems, legal challenges and weather abnormalities. We will minimise opposition (the antis get their say in Chapter Seven), we will assume an estate landlord (which is close to the norm) and we will adopt a pan-RO position, which is to say figures will be averaged across many years of the support regime without pegging them to one specific annual period.

The Scotia wind farm is medium-sized, featuring ten turbines of three megawatts each. If it is not pushing things too far, it rotates gently on the horizon in a tumbling, hypnotising way that neither distracts from the wider elements of the landscape nor trespasses beyond the wedge of its immediate viewshed. It is an idyll and an ideal of the wind farm form, which admittedly does not improve the economics but which nevertheless ticks a number of boxes in the imagination of the author.

Total investment to build our generic project was somewhere between £30 million and £45 million. Roughly 80 per cent of the upfront cost was the wind turbines themselves (imported, so victim to exchange rate fluctuations) with the remainder of capital expenditure going to balance of plant civil engineering works, electric infrastructure and connections. The headline figures do not include the cost of development, which also wraps around the expense of consent and pre-construction items, which would probably be an additional £1.5 million to £2 million, give or take.

Gross revenues once constructed are fairly straightforward. A decent Scottish wind farm built in the RO era will at £100 per megawatt-hour (wholesale plus support payment) produce around £250,000 per megawatt per annum in sales, although some obviously bring in more and some less. Scotia's ten turbines will therefore produce roughly £7.5 million in gross sales in a 'normal' year, ie one that was neither too calm nor too windy, and during which significant maintenance issues were absent. Assuming an operational life of 20 years (below the industry baseline, but the term of RO contracts) the total revenue during operations at our wind farm will be £150 million.

There are of course many bills to pay.

Finance is a major element for most wind farms, with the exception of the big utilities and other cash-rich companies that can build off balance sheet. Assuming 80 per cent debt at Scotia to be paid off over 15 years at 7.5 per cent (a perhaps slightly optimistic but not outrageous proposition), the total annual repayments during the term of the loan would be between £2.6 million and £4 million.

Other items also eat into gross revenues. Every project has associated operational and maintenance expenses while there are additional regular outgoings including but not limited to

MYTH 4

Wind is expensive

Onshore wind over its lifetime is currently the cheapest way to produce utility-scale electricity from a newbuild power technology. That's all, no matter how you slice it.

business rates and other taxes, power trading costs, management fees, insurances, charges to use the grid, accounting expenses, community benefits (£150,000 per annum at Scotia; love thy neighbour) and rent payments to the landlord. These will be, as a very rough rule of thumb, equivalent to 5 per cent of capital expenditure each year.

When all the outgoings from Scotia are tallied, the total bill is between roughly £2.5 million and £3 million in annual costs, which means that during the first 15 years of operation (while also paying off the original debt) total profit would be at least £7.5 million, with the last five years of RO eligibility adding a further £22.5 million – assuming all went well with the ageing turbines. Post-RO production will complicate the picture, so we will assume decommissioning at the end of 20 years which will require an additional one-off cost but still leave overall lifetime profits at greater than £25 million, representing an overall profit margin of better than 20 per cent.

That is pretty good going and, because we have created a perfect project operating at peak RO, it probably over-represents what most wind farms would actually generate in terms of cash. There are, however, at least a handful of large-scale projects, with exceptionally wind-rich and straightforward build locations, which made and continue to make better returns. It is also worth mentioning that the bigger the wind farm, the more economies of scale come into play. If you extrapolate the basics of our simple illustration to a megafarm like SSE's 522 megawatt Clyde in the south-west or Scottish Power's 539 megawatt Whitelee outside of Glasgow – where items on the debit side would be squeezed – you begin to see how lucrative wind can be and, in fact, is.

Utilities during the period between 2004 and 2015 were largely uninterested in projects that failed to achieve rates of return of 15 per cent, while most independent companies during the meat of the obligation era would turn their backs on wind farms with anything less than a ten per cent rate of return. Consented pre-construction developments were regularly trading hands for tens of millions of pounds; for companies or individuals that could successfully drive a project through planning and offer the market a shovel-ready option, fortunes were often made overnight.

It should be acknowledged that, despite what some critics of the industry might say, there is nothing inherently wrong with making money out of renewable energy; wind power is a business like any other and the developers then as now were playing by the rules established by government policy and interpreted by the market. Few question the rights or wrongs of the profits attached to fossil fuel generation, of the utilities and the network companies that have always taken their cut from providing power to consumers and businesses. What is wrong with making money out of wind turbines? The answer for opponents and sceptics was linked to the RO itself. The structure of the mechanism meant that roughly 45 per cent of revenues accrued by the onshore part of the wind industry were being paid by consumers via their electricity bills. Questions began to be asked very soon after the policy was enacted about what exactly society was getting in return for this investment, concerns only amplified by the financial crisis of 2007–8 and the subsequent hit to living standards.

A key battlefield was employment. Industry and government both promised repeatedly through the early years of the onshore revolution that new jobs would result from the deployment of Scottish wind power projects. The pitch at its most basic, and oft-repeated, was that money used to support renewables via the RO would spur investment in the supply chain akin to what had been happening in Denmark, Germany and Spain; an implied social contract of 'subsidy equals jobs', intentional or otherwise, was soon created.

And employment was indeed arriving: developers, consultants, service providers, lawyers and engineers were all hiring across Scotland. However, the holy grail of industrial expansion, manufacturing jobs, proved elusive. This despite a number of sincere attempts to make wind work at a nuts and bolts level in Great Britain.

Danish turbine manufacturer Vestas, one of the global leaders in the industry, established a UK business at Machrihanish near Campbeltown on the Kintyre peninsula in the early 2000s. The Scandinavian outfit was one of a number of European companies which had run the numbers on the UK market and the only company that determined there was money to be made from the outset by setting up shop locally. In the specific case of what became Vestas Celtic, financial support from Highlands and Islands Enterprise also helped turn its head. The agency spent nearly £12 million upgrading a former west coast RAF base to make it an attractive location for business and paid the new tenant £578,000 for skills and development work.

Mark Powell started what was a 16-year career with the Danish company almost by accident, having been born and raised in Leeds before moving north of the border to indulge a passion for rock-climbing as a fringe benefit to his job in the industrial ceramics sector. His then girlfriend, later wife, had secured a job in Campbeltown that lured the couple away from their Fife home. 'Vestas Celtic was hiring for the sales team. I didn't have the relevant experience in the slightest, having previously only sold things that were worth pennies apiece. This was a whole different prospect, but at that point if you had half a brain and a pulse they'd give you a shot. Machrihanish was a hard place to attract people to. I decided to throw the dice.'

The ex-RAF facility, in addition to the sales and admin activities, also manufactured towers and assembled nacelles. The latter entails taking the separate components that make up the guts of the turbine – drivetrain, generator etc – and installing them within the housing that sits atop every turbine. Those assembled units, which look a bit like caravans without windows, are then installed in one lift.

Within a few years of opening, it became apparent that Machrihanish was the wrong place for nacelle assembly. 'There was a recognition that local manufacturing made sense, but more for towers than anything,' said Powell of the facility some three hours from Glasgow by lorry. 'Nacelles were a value-dense thing (in terms of the money invested) to be shipping in and out of the back roads of Kintyre and the west of Scotland.'

The company's Scottish toehold, and around 100 related jobs, did not last much longer; Vestas Celtic opened an office in Warrington in northern England in the mid-2000s into which the sales and admin activities were increasingly concentrated, and in summer 2008 the Danish HQ decided to pull the plug on all activities at Machrihanish. Vestas said at the time: 'The products for which the factory was designed and streamlined do not generate satisfactory earnings'; the remote location was out of step with the Danes' increasingly lean global supply chain.

A rollercoaster ride then followed.

Vestas' compatriot Skykon stepped into the breach in 2009 hoping to expand operations four-fold on the back of client diversification and the addition of component production for the nascent offshore wind sector. However, the company ran into financial difficulties the following year and eventually filed for bankruptcy in early 2011.

Next to take the reins was a consortium including Marsh Global (another company with links to the Danish wind supply chain), development agency HIE and utility SSE. The Perth-headquartered company via turbine supplier Siemens had a direct interest in seeing tower contracts for its under-construction Clyde wind farm completed at the factory, while HIE was once again looking to promote development on the Kintyre peninsula and safeguard jobs, this time through a £3.4 million, 19.9 per cent equity stake in the manufacturer.

Five years later, Korean company CS Wind paid an undisclosed price to take full control of the business with a

Muck and brass: the less glamorous side of the wind boom, including civil engineering such as foundations, should not be ignored in any consideration of the employment picture.
With kind permission of Infinergy Ltd

promise to invest £14 million and expand the workforce to 200, largely through continued expansion into the offshore wind sector. They remain the owner at the time of writing, albeit the company was forced to make significant cuts to the workforce at the tail end of 2019 due to the emergence of a gap in their order book. Next steps are unclear.

The revolving door of business plans, shareholders and owners was replicated at a number of other yards and supply chain businesses around Scotland, most notably at Arnish on Lewis which hosted a series of manufacturing efforts for onshore and offshore wind as well as marine renewables. Across the country, securing wind-related manufacturing jobs seemed like an uphill battle, while the pinnacle achievement of a turbine manufacturing facility, and its many hundreds of positions, seemed nigh on impossible.

A combination of factors was to blame. The first was scale: the RO years represented an unprecedented expansion of wind in Scotland and the rest of the UK but the annual market was small in global terms; it simply did not have the project pipeline to justify the sorts of investment necessary to build a major manufacturing facility.

Second was timing. The Scottish wind power boom mirrored similar growth elsewhere around the globe. Markets such as the US and China were achieving stratospheric installation volumes by comparison to what was being achieved in Scotland and soaking up investment in plant and capacity. Simultaneously, many countries in Europe continued a longer and stronger tradition of deployment and they already boasted established production facilities that were more than capable of meeting demand from development in the UK.

Finally, the wind sector was fast maturing. Manufacturers and the related supply chain were shifting away from an almost evangelical focus on market share as measured by the number of turbines sold or installed. Replacing the mantra of 'more wind is good for business' was the pursuit of pure profitability; production was as a result increasingly centralised and at scale, and moving more often than not to where labour was cheapest.

The wind industry in Scotland, with the public demanding a very obvious and direct boost to employment, made a final and substantial attempt to swim against the tide.

In 2008, heavy-hitting utilities and developers including SSE, Scottish Power, Amec, Airtricity, RES, Fred Olsen Renewables, RDC and Npower joined forces with an offer designed to encourage a major turbine manufacturer to set up shop in Scotland. The Framework Agreement for Scottish Turbines, known of course as FAST, dangled as a reward the potential to supply a 5,000 megawatt pipeline in the long term – many times the total of onshore wind installed in the country at that time and worth many billions of pounds in possible sales.

Potential suppliers were required to promise Scottish

content not only in terms of putting turbines together – the same 'assembly' carried out in the early years of Vestas Celtic – but also the manufacture of headline components such as gearboxes, drivetrains and blades, all the way down to the smallest nut or circuit board. One of the FAST members said at the time: 'Suppliers need to respond. Potential component companies need to respond. We need a pull from them as well as this push from us. What we are looking to do here is have something proposed that is substantial: a global manufacturing facility.'

Political support was strong in principle but stumbling blocks were significant, most notably in the shape of uncertainty over future planning permissions. German turbine manufacturer Repower was eventually selected by the FAST partners but no deal was ever done. Developers could not guarantee a set volume of sales because those projects in planning, which made up the majority of the promised pipeline, remained an unknown quantity.

According to (then) Scotland Energy Minister Jim Mather:

> We are providing a supportive framework for
> commercial investment in renewables, including wind,
> through our challenging target(s)… and through
> planning reform which is bringing increased certainty
> to developers.

That level of certainty, however, was not sufficient to nail down the deal with Repower. Thousands of megawatts of potential projects, it seemed, was too far and risky a journey from the same volume of wind farms with an unqualified permission to build. One wind veteran, speaking at the time, expressed his dismay at the outcome: 'This was our last chance with manufacturing for onshore wind, make no mistake.' With the exception of the ongoing works at Machrihanish, that pronouncement proved to be prescient, and the onshore wind industry lost an easy win with the public.

Other elements of the social contract were more successful.

Community benefit was an obvious and, for most people, welcome plus, even while being described as a blatant bribe by anti-wind campaigners. The vast majority of projects built in Scotland established annual payments based on so many thousands of pounds per installed megawatt, which was distributed either to the immediate neighbours or a wider geographical spread, depending on exact circumstances, for spending as desired. Standard payments in recent years were pegged at £5,000 per megawatt per annum, although in the early years of the RO the figures were much lower.

It must be acknowledged that community benefit payments remain a small percentage of earnings at any wind farm; there have been regular calls for a much higher level of commitment from the industry and discussions about a different revenue-sharing formula based on output or income. That said, the money that has been paid out since the beginning of the wind era is substantial and in some areas transformative. There are a few communities in particularly wind-rich areas that actually have difficulty spending all of their annual payments, although that is very much the exception rather than the norm. Other direct social benefits in the wind sector locker include discounted electricity within a certain distance of a wind farm, delivery of specific investment in local assets or aspirations (a new village hall, upgraded infrastructure etc), or the opportunity to invest directly in commercial-scale projects. The latter has at times been used as a peg to append 'community' onto the name of the related wind project, even if somewhat disingenuously given the relatively modest size of the stakes involved. In other cases the monicker is more deserved, with say one of eight turbines owned directly by local or regional investors.

Landowners also benefited from the wind boom. Rents for projects in the early years of Scottish onshore were equivalent

Jobs boom: while Scotland largely missed out on the manufacturing side of the wind equation, significant employment was nevertheless created in other areas, including development, realisation (component delivery, pictured) and operation.
With kind permission of Infinergy Ltd

Scottish vs Global Growth of Wind Energy

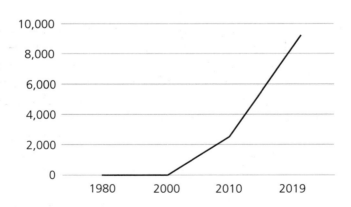

Sources: Global Wind Energy Council,
Scottish Government (BEIS)

to around two per cent of annual revenues, rose to between 4 and 5 per cent through most of the RO and peaked as high as 10 per cent in some cases during the height of the boom years around 2011–2. Contracts were often based on a mix of per-megawatt installed payments and a set slice of earnings based on actual production. Estates, big farms and other large landholders such as Forestry Commission Scotland (now Forestry and Land Scotland) and Scottish Water were among the big winners from direct payments.

All told, figures measuring the overall economic benefit of the wind sector, admittedly compiled by or on behalf of various parts of the industry, suggest that spending in Scotland over the lifetime of an onshore project will total somewhere around £1.5 million per megawatt installed. That is roughly half of the overall total spending including development, construction and operations from the first scribble of a turbine location on a section of map to the final turn of the rotor. A further 15 to 20 per cent will be spent in the rest of the UK, with the remainder going to Europe or farther afield.

The total economic boost is equivalent to £12 billion over the 40-year lifespan of the existing installed Scottish fleet, representing an average contribution of £300 million per annum (based on operational dates for individual projects spread from 1995 through 2035, but obviously much higher in years where more projects are online). Even given the unsuccessful push for manufacturing jobs, which would have lifted the local content figure much higher, most neutral observers would agree the numbers represent a sizeable and important sector of the economy.

On the other side of the societal cost and benefit equation, figures compiled by Ofgem suggest that onshore wind farms in Scotland receive some £700 million in RO payments each year, although that is a rough 'back of an envelope' calculation by the author. That total support is spread across UK billpayers, which means that consumers north of the border pay around

£85 million to directly support Scottish onshore wind; in other words, and in extremely simple terms that admittedly gloss over all kinds of complicated factors and the usual ifs and buts, the country gets £3.50 in return for every £1 it spends on large-scale, land-based wind. You can of course dilute that return by including further spending by Scottish consumers to support offshore wind, onshore projects elsewhere in the UK, other eligible technologies and support regimes such as feed-in tariffs etc, but at the most basic level the people living north of the border get more in economic benefit than they spend supporting onshore wind. Whether that is an acceptable level of return, and whether that is fair in the wider UK context given that the remainder of the union does not fare so well from the same maths, depends very much on who is doing the judging and how they view the low carbon imperative.

Among the population at large, there are those who believe the 'greening' of electricity on its own justifies ongoing investment via the RO and that any associated benefits are simply an added bonus. But there are also of course other opinions: some are adamant zero public spending should be devoted to curbing emissions and it should be left to the free market to regulate itself; there are arguments about the relative merits of the existing flat-rate consumer levy compared with the alternative of meeting the cost of the carbon fight via the more progressive route of the tax system; there are associated debates both genuine and frivolous about the efficacy of wind, the role of nuclear, the reality of climate change, what possible difference a small country like Scotland can make to what is a global problem.

Political arguments on both sides of the border reflected the full range of opinions on offer. All agreed the Renewables Oblgiation had been wildly successful in encouraging deployment of projects across Scotland and the rest of the UK, with Westminster and Holyrood's ever-increasing green energy targets for the electricity sector regularly being met and/or surpassed. And that perception of a bit of breathing space in the climate war, real or otherwise, meant there was an opportunity to fine-tune/tinker/ overhaul/scrap (delete according to party preference) the support policies that had been so successful to date.

Ministers in Edinburgh were all for letting the good times roll; the renewables success story was leapfrogging from onshore into marine energy, offshore wind and floating turbines. The continued expansion represented what Holyrood considered an immense opportunity for the country and an investment worth continuing.

Westminster also acknowledged the potentially dazzling upside of the sector. However, the arrival of austerity, combined with disquiet in some quarters over the rise – and rise and rise – of onshore wind and other renewables, convinced those in charge in London that it was time to drive a much harder bargain with the sector.

The days of unlimited horizons, and what was increasingly considered freewheel spending by some of those with their hands on the levers of policy, were coming to an end.

6

The End of the Beginning

AS THE SECOND decade of the new millennium took root, questions about the broad push for ever-increasing amounts of renewable generation were beginning to be asked more regularly at Scottish and UK level. A number of politicians particularly on the right were uncomfortable about the speed and scope of development as well as the amount of money necessary to keep the RO bandwagon rolling.

The immediate purpose of the nearly ten-year-old mechanism, to kickstart large-scale decarbonisation of the electricity system via renewables, was functioning as planned. Transformation of the energy sector was marching forward and onshore wind was leading the way, with other technologies particularly offshore wind and solar starting to play their part.

However, the relatively limitless horizons of the RO and the pressure – modified with adjective of choice depending on political preferences – the regime was putting on consumers via electricity bills were at odds with the increasingly acute austerity sparked by the global banking crisis of 2008. With the arrival of a Conservative-Liberal Democrat coalition at Westminster in 2010 the value of decarbonisation via renewable energy was no longer a given; Prime Minister David Cameron was famously quoted as telling aides to 'get rid of all the green crap' in energy bills to drive down costs (a quote Downing Street never disowned, saying instead it did not 'recognise' the phrase). Nuclear climbed the agenda in the new Cabinet as the most cost-effective way to meet emissions goals.

The situation in Scotland was markedly different. The independence and independently minded Scottish National Party had taken the reins at Holyrood in 2007 as a minority administration and in the 2011 election translated their increasing support among the electorate into an outright majority. The SNP, like its predecessors in Edinburgh, embraced renewables for the economic opportunities on offer, albeit not all members were enthusiastic: some of its MSPs, and parts of its grassroots base, had at times been openly hostile to renewable energy in general and onshore wind in particular (and some still are).

Holyrood under the SNP had nevertheless put its faith instead in large-scale wind, wave and tidal arrays alongside emerging technologies such as utility-scale biomass and carbon capture and storage while being overtly opposed to new nuclear. Alex Salmond, First Minister between 2007 and 2014, famously predicted the country would become the 'Saudi Arabia of renewables'. No plan was too far-fetched, no potential inward investment underplayed, no prototype installation un-encouraged; Scotland in some ways became a playground for the 'what might be possible' in a decarbonised world.

The diverging interests north and south of the border would eventually reach breaking point – as detailed in Chapter Ten – but in the immediate term the varying political outlooks found common ground in the requirement to craft a replacement for the Renewables Obligation that would allow for ongoing development of sectors including onshore wind, but at a reduced price for consumers.

Westminster legislation was first mooted in 2010 and eventually introduced in November 2012. Holyrood provided its broad blessing for the new Energy Bill on the basis that Scottish interests would play an active role in shaping the associated implementation policies around what would be called Electricity Market Reform, which were expected to benefit all comers but particularly those north of the border.

In a formal statement following publication of the draft legislation, Edinburgh officials welcomed the inclusion of what they understood to be 'statutory requirement to consult Scottish ministers on the design and delivery' of the new mechanism. Cross-border cooperation was both offered and expected: 'We have established a set of principles under which we will work together during the first delivery plan in both the analytical and decision-making phase.'

Salmond said in an accompanying letter: 'I am clear that to maintain the considerable momentum in the renewables industry in Scotland, the... framework must provide the same degree of ongoing market certainty that the RO delivers – and which is accelerating the development and deployment of renewable technologies both in Scotland and the rest of the UK.'

He added: 'When I have sufficient assurance that the right levels of support will be available for the technologies where Scotland has natural advantages, I will decide whether and to what extent we need to maintain the RO in Scotland.'

Edinburgh's heartfelt belief that Scotland was in control of its own renewables destiny would in time turn out to be badly mistaken. Many working in the sector north of the border believe to this day that Holyrood was naive to trust Westminster in good faith in the subsequent policy deliberations; the Scottish government essentially handed over control of future policy in return for an empty promise, those critics argue.

But we are getting ahead of ourselves. The Energy Act 2013 received royal assent in December of that year and Secretary of State for Energy Ed Davey, a LibDem, said the legislation would 'attract investment to bring about a once in a generation transformation of our electricity market'.

Key among the new initiatives was a shift towards competitive auctions for eligible projects through a mechanism known as Contracts for Difference. In very basic terms, the CfD established a maximum support level – the strike price – which set a ceiling for payments based on individual technologies

MYTH 5

Wind farms negatively impact tourism

Repeated studies have found that tourism and wind farms can happily co-exist, and that turbines do not have a direct impact on holiday decisions. Denmark has loads of turbines (even Copenhagen has numerous wind assets) and a thriving tourism sector.

There is some evidence that people with strong anti-wind feelings, and those seeking to escape all elements of modern life, will avoid areas with wind farms. On the flip side, several wind farm visitor centres have become well-established attractions – the one at Scottish Power's operational Whitelee project outside Glasgow has had 500,000 visitors since the doors opened in 2009.

and their perceived market readiness (or otherwise). Subsidies would 'float' to top up the wholesale price of electricity, rather than simply being bolted on top of the market at a set rate, as with the RO. Onshore was capped at £95 per megawatt (all-in) for projects going live in 2014–5, compared with £155 for offshore wind, £305 for wave or tidal, £100 for hydro and £120 for solar. An overall limit for spending across all projects in any one auction round was also established.

Developers seeking to build a wind farm under the CfD submitted a price bid into a competitive auction and, subsequent to machinations that do not require detailing, were successful if the supports sought were lower or equal when compared with other participants. In general, the cheaper the overall level of supports sought by industry, the more projects would proceed. Certain criteria such as planning permission were required before a wind farm could be submitted into the auction, designed in part to prevent the failures of the NFFO/SRO auction regime of the 1990s when a percentage of winning projects were never built.

The outcome of the first round was announced on 26 February 2014. Offshore wind, including a project in the Firth of Forth, was very much the star of the show, but 15 onshore wind farms totalling 750 megawatts secured contracts for delivery before 2020, with ten of those located in Scotland and representing around two-thirds of the total capacity. The prices awarded were £82.50 per megawatt hour with the exception of a single project going forward at £79.99; a healthy if not jaw-dropping discount to the roughly £90 per megawatt-hour represented by the wholesale price of electricity plus the RO boost during that same period.

Wind developers grumbled in public but most appeared ready to work with the new system. The CfD as mapped by the legislation was designed to run in tandem with the RO for the first 30 months of its existence before the latter mechanism was closed to new entrants in March 2017. New projects would then be built only under the follow-on regime, pending a successful bid into regular allocation auctions, and prices would continue to fall during an envisaged smooth and gradual transition period that over time would result in the construction of turbine arrays requiring no supports. The electricity system would continue to be 'greened', the low carbon economy would thrive, consumers would pay less.

Things did not quite work out that way. On which note, it is time to introduce the Antis.

7

Antis, Nimbys and Other Opposition – Plus the Grid

NOT EVERYBODY WAS happy about the wind power revolution.

'I received a letter on 1 March 2006 from (the UK arm of German developer) Energiekontor about plans for 13 turbines at Gathercauld,' said Graham Lang, a Fife resident originally in sales but in more recent years the chair of wind action group Scotland Against Spin.

'We have big windows facing due south right at the site where the wind farm was planned. The turbines were going to be 85 metres high and the nearest just 600 yards away; absolutely horrific,' he remembered of the development near Ceres.

He added in the 'planning-speak' that becomes second nature to those on either side of the battle lines: 'I was trying to protect our residential, landscape and visual amenity.'

Lang and other self-described 'concerned residents' formed the Ceres and District Environment and Amenity Protection Group, CADEAP, and mustered 300 local people to attend a village hall consultation event.

Developer and meeting host Energiekontor had already acted on initial reactions to its plans by cutting its proposed Gathercauld project to five turbines with a reduction in height of five metres, but this cut no ice with the group. 'All developers over-egg plans at the start so there's room to be seen to be addressing concerns,' said Lang matter-of-factly.

He did not warm to what he called an 'obnoxious' PR effort

on behalf of the developer; CADEAP instead met with local authority elected representatives and community councils, raised money and funded its own studies into landscape impacts, noise, geological conditions. Lang bought Energiekontor shares so he could travel to the company's annual general meeting in Germany and raise his concerns directly with the board.

The group filed a detailed objection and, despite a positive recommendation from planning department officials from Fife Council, members of the North East Fife Area Committee voted 13 to 1 in summer 2009 to refuse the wind farm. Energiekontor, some might say unusually, decided not to appeal the decision.

Following the success, said Lang, he became something of a 'go-to person' for anyone seeking advice on opposing applications and on the wind industry in general. Along with a few others, he eventually formalised his role within Communities Against Turbines, or CATS, before moving on to establish SAS in January 2013.

The organisation describes itself as 'an independent alliance campaigning for the reform of the Scottish government's unsustainable wind energy policy'. It boasts a professional-looking website with up to the minute updates on planning applications, other news relevant to the wind sector and a digital library of resources designed to arm anyone interested in fighting a wind farm.

SAS is far from being the first of its kind. Anti group Views of Scotland was formed as long ago as 2002 with a mission to educate the public, highlight wind issues and 'drum some sense' into the political sector. Like most organisations of a similar ilk, it loudly proclaimed that it had no problem with renewables as an asset class; it simply preferred wave and tidal power over what it described at the time as the 'unproven' wind sector.

Seventeen years later, Lang echoed the sentiment. 'A diverse energy supply is very sensible. A carbon-free society seems to be the way it is going, I'm not a Luddite,' he said. 'But the

Protest artist: campaigner Graham Lang took up his paintbrush as part of a multi-pronged battle against plans for the Gathercauld wind farm in Fife.
Courtesy of Graham Lang

important part for wind farms is that they are "in their place", as the Scottish government says.'

He paused before adding of the policy: 'Of course that's complete and utter cobblers.'

Lang was disparaging but at least policy-specific; others are not so discriminating. There is a small but notable crossover in some parts of the Anti movement that conflate opposition to onshore wind and other renewables with arguments over nationalism; and there appears to be no middle ground on either.

A new addition to our village who discovered I was writing this book, and to be fair I have no idea where he sits on the scale of nimbyism or independence, recently offered the uninvited opinion that the history of Scottish onshore could be summed up as 'thankfully very short before it disappeared along with that (insert derogatory phrase of choice) SNP'. The new arrival in question filled those brackets with a disparaging historic reference suggesting the party was some way short of believing in the merits of democratic government, and unaccustomed to acting within its limits, but specifics have been omitted in the name of keeping the peace when I take the bins to the kerb.

It may have been a nervous and inappropriate gaffe, or perhaps he really was hoping to influence the narrative by being slightly outrageous. The comment is in either case the sort of combative and ill-informed throwaway that is all too commonplace in the polarised political climate of the ongoing independence debate in Scotland. It should be noted for the record that while support for wind development certainly reached its apex under the Scottish National Party at Holyrood, the Conservatives introduced the SRO and Labour the basis of the RO, both at Westminster level, while broader energy markets have long been a UK-wide concern.

Various administrations in Edinburgh have embraced the growth of wind, and have implemented policies to ensure Scotland was heavily involved, but those efforts largely straddled the divide over independence. The Scottish Tories are really the only party at Holyrood to have regularly raised concerns about the expansion of the sector.

On the UK stage, there are established campaign organisations that have questioned wind as part of much wider efforts to counter arguments about climate change and energy choices; prime among those are the Renewable Energy Foundation and the Global Warming Policy Foundation. The two groups certainly played a role in shaping policy arguments at Westminster, and created many column inches of coverage, but as a general rule that did not play particularly well in Scotland and appears not to have had a huge impact on the majority of the body politic.

The most effective lobbying north of the border was carried out at the hyper-local level, by the project-specific campaign groups such as the Gathercauld-focused CADEAP, driven by immediate reactions to the possible introduction of large-scale infrastructure into an area that may have been largely unchanged for decades, or to a favoured rural landscape or viewpoint.

Dogmatic and far-reaching anti-wind positions were often adopted thereafter, certainly, and the fight taken onto a bigger stage via VOS, CATS, SAS and their ilk, often encouraged by cross-fertilisation between Anti groups in Scotland, the UK and internationally. But it was the buzz, rush and, yes, camaraderie experienced during the initial Anti battles on the home front that often spurred involvement in the wider war. Those seeking to understand the opposition movement should never underestimate the lure of that belonging.

Broad-based special interest organisations, both regularly lobbied by the antis and courted by the wind industry itself, took a more systematic approach to onshore development.

The John Muir Trust, acting in the name of the renowned Scottish-American environmentalist, was established to 'defend wild land, enhance habitats and encourage people of all ages and backgrounds to connect with wild places'. In the context of wind, that means objecting to what the organisation describes as 'industrial large-scale developments' in wild land areas across Scotland.

Policy officer John Low, a former head teacher with a background in outdoor education, said the Trust is 'committed to the emissions targets of the UK and Scottish government', that it only objects to a small percentage of projects, but that 'you don't save one thing by destroying another thing'.

The organisation believes large-scale wind is more appropriate to 'brownfield sites reasonably close to areas of population demand', while areas near more pristine landscapes are better suited for 'sensitively-sited, community-scale renewable energy schemes which demonstrate that renewable energy may be produced without significantly affecting wild lands and are reasonably adjacent to existing settlements.'

The Trust defines community scale as producing the energy production equivalent to the needs of area residents, rather than by any particular share of ownership or associated financial benefit.

Onshore wind farm development through the RO era was driven by 'profit and not people', said Low, in part because of what he believes was a complete lack of a coherent and wide-ranging energy plan at either UK or Scottish level. The establishment of defined wild land areas in Scotland over the last ten years has helped to focus the arguments, he added, but that did not mean the fight was won. 'The struggle will go on endlessly, if it is against wind farms or something else.'

The Trust believes the playing field could in part be levelled if public bodies such as the Scottish government or local authorities were responsible for commissioning environmental assessments for wind farm projects, rather than the documentation being produced at the behest of the developers. 'Whoever pays the piper calls the tune,' said Low. 'The change would introduce some neutrality.'

Outdoor organisation Mountaineering Scotland works on behalf of its hillwalking, climbing and snow-touring members to among other things protect mountain landscapes. Ongoing concerns include hard-edge forestry plantation, hill tracks, hydro-electric infrastructure and, of course, large-scale onshore wind. It frames the question of renewables developments such as wind farms within the context of ethics, aesthetics and economics.

The organisation accepts the need to move to a low-carbon economy and, it points out, only objects to a small proportion of proposals, around one in 20, 'that are potentially the most damaging'.

Mountaineering Scotland believes the planning system often fails to strike the right balance between development and protection, in large part because efforts have focused on a

Sign language: a wind farm protester gets creative for a protest event in Inverness in March 2013.
Courtesy Scotland Against Spin

quantitative rather than qualitative approach that is ill-suited to assessing what is being lost. 'You can count how many skylarks there are, for instance, but how do you measure landscape? There is no Annex 1 listing for landscape like there is for protected species,' it said.

Wind is particularly damaging to mountain areas, the organisation believes, because it 'stands out, shouts out, from the landscape' with a kinetic, sky-scraping aspect that does not feature on other rural infrastructure including dam heads, reservoirs, roads or buildings. It believes that contrary to some research wind farms do have a meaningful impact on tourism, particularly among those seeking to enjoy the peace of the hillside, and is having a detrimental effect on visitor numbers.

The organisations said there has been creeping industrialisation of mountain and rural landscapes over the last 20 years in part – and this is where morality comes into play – because the commercial wind sector has systematically pushed the boundaries: reducing the size of planned projects to get them through the planning system only to return afterwards to secure permission for the original footprint, asking for repeated extensions to established projects, and clustering in order to take advantage of incremental changes to an ever-shifting baseline that will eventually be classed as a wind farm landscape and so immune from the curbs on further development.

Mountaineering Scotland does not believe this is an acceptable way for the industry to behave and points to money as the main driver. It asks whether serious consideration has been given to 'how much wind we actually need in a balanced electricity system' and questions the economic case that has driven much of modern wind development in Scotland. 'Tom Johnston never filled every Highland glen with a hydro dam. What is going on now (with wind) is about export, not distribution.'

Looking ahead, the organisation is hoping for a wider

ranging consideration of energy, landscapes and development by politicians and the nation as a whole. 'Where we go from here is to discuss what we, as a civic society, wish to see in the future.'

And Mountaineering Scotland argues the gatekeepers have some catching up to do. 'There is no beauty in the planning system,' it said.

Bird charity RSPB has also been a key participant in the debate over Scottish wind, perhaps more so than any other non-governmental voice. The group's opinions on the potential impacts of any given project on various protected or other species could make or break an application, despite the lack of any 'official' weight to the guidance provided. Developers have long gone out of their way to keep RSPB happy and planners as well as other official bodies are often quick to reflect the organisation's views.

Government agency Scottish Natural Heritage (SNH), meanwhile, was not so much an opponent of the industry as it was a referee, trying to ensure wind farm projects played by the rules established to protect landscapes, wildlife and the wider environment.

SNH, which changed its name to NatureScot in 2020, is a statutory consultee, which in planning terms means it can provide opinion, advice or an objection to any application. A red card from the Inverness-based organisation will more often than not trigger an official public inquiry. Ministers on occasion rule against SNH wishes but not as a matter of course.

Its founding principles, established in the early 1990s, were to ensure sustainable development in Scotland. However, the organisation was not well prepared for the onset of the wind energy revolution in 1995–6, confronted almost overnight with new technologies, new locational requirements and against a background of what some considered a lack of clarity over government policy.

'We knew that we needed to be more strategic, locationally,

in our approach,' said Roger Crofts, who was Chief Executive of SNH between 1992 and 2002. 'We had some strategic locational experience in dealing with forestry planting applications but there was no support from government for a strategic locational approach to wind farms. This has remained the case ever since despite lobbying by SNH and many other environmental bodies.'

The only guidance provided by the Scottish Government was to 'let the market take its course,' he added, with no restrictions placed on application locations until much later on.

Crofts said in hindsight, 'The government's lack of specific direction wasted the time and money of the industry, public authorities and local communities. As a result, SNH and all of the local authorities had to address every application that came forward and local communities had to work voluntarily to find resources to challenge development applications. It was immensely frustrating.'

National-level locational guidance would have 'removed the noise and provided a strategic approach'. It never happened and, once what Crofts described as 'green politics' became involved, 'anything to shift the balance between fossil fuel electricity production was regarded as beneficial.'

The since-retired trained geographer said that if given a free hand to design a decision system from scratch for assessing wind farms, he would have established set ground rules based on inputs from the ministries of energy and the environment and including factors such as grid infrastructure, life-time energy costs and a locationally strategic approach. He then would have used that template to judge all that followed.

'We won't look at every case, we'll agree the criteria, and we'll look at those of a more strategic significance,' he said. Crofts also believes a wider conversation is necessary given the demands of green transport and renewable heat: Is wind the only solution? What is the technology telling us? 'These are really important,' he said.

As the wind sector became established, the national press at both Scottish and UK level was uncertain how to deal with the story. Was this news, politics, environment, business? It was of course all of those things but, given the structural division between different new desks and beat reporters, the wind industry tended to get the seven blind men and an elephant treatment – coverage was fine as far as it related to individual elements, but rarely did the reader get an overview of the wider issues.

Much of the English-based mainstream media was anti as a default position; *The Daily Telegraph*, *Daily Mail*, *Daily Express* and *The Times*, as well as the associated Scottish editions, were the most negative, but even the liberal *Guardian* found it difficult to square broad green concerns with the apparently contrasting requirement to build large metal structures in rural locations and, perhaps most hand-wringingly for some metropolitans, at a profit.

Columnists often led the charge. The late Christopher Booker penned articles such as 'Wind farms: the monuments to lunacy', 'We're following Germany to an energy disaster', 'No, wind power is not the cheapest form of energy', 'The lights may go out'. Fellow commentator James Delingpole has described renewables in print as 'an expensive joke', a 'great fraud', a 'farce' and, my playing-to-the-gallery favourite as headlined by website Breitbart News, 'Study: Wind farms are even more expensive and pointless than you thought'.

Environmentalist and regular *Guardian* contributor George Monbiot, a more constructive observer but still sometime critic, warned as early as 2007 that onshore wind had reached saturation point in parts of the UK, and suggested that all future projects should be built at sea. 'Beyond having a few more wind farms, [further onshore projects] will generate so much antagonism it'll turn people off dealing with climate change,' he told reporters at the Hay Festival in May that year.

He added some years later that the spread of onshore wind

was forcing people into 'backwards reasoning' to deny the very basis for the construction of more land-based turbines. 'Many of those who deny that climate change is taking place reached that position as a result of their opposition to wind farms,' he wrote.

The Scottish press was divided. *The Scotsman* and *The Press & Journal* more often than not ran negative stories about the onshore wind sector, while *The Herald* largely took the editorial decision to treat wind power as a business story or, if it was a wider picture, as part of the environment beat. *The Courier* out of Dundee took on wind development as a news story with a generally neutral approach, while local papers up and down Scotland were largely negative towards onshore development both in terms of news and opinion. The tabloids tended to stay away from wind until it reached its most sensational, with coverage to match.

Influence from the Anti campaigns on media of all stripes should not be underestimated. The groups both local and national were vocal, committed, well-organised and they assaulted newsdesks with a well-established and unrivalled network of letter writers, tipsters and agenda-influencers. They punched well above their weight and convinced many a reporter that what might seem like a minority, outlying position was in fact just common sense. The worst of the antis could also, and here I speak from personal experience, be extremely aggressive, belligerent and threatening. They would sometimes refuse to take no for an answer, so convinced were they of the correctness of their outlook and position. More usually, though, it was a matter of politely but firmly trying to outflank, rather than intimidate.

Online planning application databases as established at both Holyrood and local authority level became a key weapon in the Anti armoury: dig out early correspondence with officials, an application for a met mast, initial scoping report documentation, and get the fight against a new wind farm development rolling from the earliest stage. Ditto with appeal decisions; the window for legal challenges was finite and early notice was important for those looking to take their grievances before a judge.

Some project developers waged a quiet and, to the outsider, entertaining war of terminology. As the Antis became more sophisticated, an increasing number of planning applications no longer included searchable phrases such as 'wind farm' or 'wind turbine', but rather adopted a range of descriptions to sidestep early detection. Exact locations were disguised, scale and scope buried in obscure, sometimes tangential terminology. Beating the Antis to the initial punch, whether at community consultation events or community council meetings, allowed developers to frame their own story, rather than reacting from behind the curve to a narrative established by opponents to the industry.

It was all part of a never-ending fight, according to Lang. 'You don't win the war really, you win just a few battles.'

Looking back, the campaigner believes there should have been dedicated, concentrated zones established for onshore wind in areas where there would be minimum impact on communities and any issues arising could be addressed through planning. 'The Scottish landscape is very important,' he said.

He does believe the days of what he called 'adhoc development' are done. 'In 2010 there were applications everywhere you looked, it became a bit of a feeding frenzy. Speculative people aren't in it now, just the major electricity generation companies.' Going forward, he believes 'the west is safe' but, given recent support for so-called remote applications, 'the islands will be ruined'.

His overall view of the sector, after all the years spent fighting, is best typified as one of otherness, of a world apart, succinctly reflected by his summary of the long-time foe: 'It was a really weird bunch that wanted to build wind farms.'

As an aside, some Anti fights extended to the grid network,

which is both separate from but intrinsic to wind power.

Separate because decisions on transmission or distribution system upgrades and extensions are carried out on a system-wide basis to meet the needs of the wider energy system; intrinsic because those works have over the last 25 years more often than not been carried out to accommodate turbines connecting to the national or local grid network.

As a result of the latter, much of the fury surrounding onshore wind has also migrated into fights over power lines, lattice towers and wooden poles, the logic being that if you can stop the wires carrying electricity from remote locations to where the people are, you can stop the wind farms.

The controversial upgrade of the Beauly to Denny transmission line between the Highlands and the Central Belt, eventually completed in 2015, is without question the most high-profile of those ding-dongs, but there are plenty of other examples.

Power lines are an unavoidable part of modern life. They are like roads and mass housing and supermarkets; we may not always appreciate the architecture but the utility, in the most basic form of the word, is undeniable.

The growth of renewables has of course necessitated a change in how the grid network should work. A system built on a small number of very large power producers requires a different configuration of wires than one designed to accommodate a very large number of smaller generators.

That evolution is currently somewhere in the middle of its journey, neither in the concentrated mode where it was so comfortable for so long nor in the completely localised, dispersed philosophy often championed by the earliest wind proponents. Complicating the picture are advances in how the grid is managed, which changes the formula of what is possible and/or desirable.

A separate book would be required to consider the full history and implications of renewables on the grid and,

Scottish Renewable Generation as Percentage of UK Totals

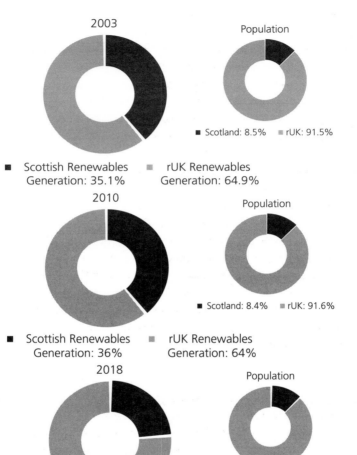

2003

Population

■ Scotland: 8.5%   ■ rUK: 91.5%

■ Scottish Renewables   ■ rUK Renewables
  Generation: 35.1%   Generation: 64.9%

2010

Population

■ Scotland: 8.4%   ■ rUK: 91.6%

■ Scottish Renewables   ■ rUK Renewables
  Generation: 36%   Generation: 64%

2018

Population

■ Scotland: 8.2%   ■ rUK: 91.8%

■ Scottish Renewables   ■ rUK Renewables
  Generation: 23.8%   Generation: 76.2%

Source: Scottish Government Energy
Statistics Database (BEIS), ONS UK.

given that would require significant technical know-how and expertise, it will not be written by this author. However, for this consideration of Scottish wind, and because the picture would be incomplete without at least a short mention, it is important to note three things:

1. The UK grid system was always going to require a serious revamp as the country's previous generation of plant aged and was replaced, be that by renewables, nuclear, gas, hydrogen, fairy moondust or some other solution.

2. Onshore wind – love or hate it – helped facilitate and pay for a long-overdue evolution of the grid network, including its expansion into areas of the country where it was under-developed, massively beyond its sell-by date, and/or non-existent.

3. Adjacent, new, exciting and/or promising technologies such as offshore wind, carbon capture and storage, marine energy, tidal barrages and EV charging have already or soon will benefit from the advances to the grid system originally delivered in large part to meet the demands of onshore wind.

It is also worth a quick detour to consider constraint payments, which are made to project owners when system operator National Grid directs a generator to go offline in order to keep the electricity network behaving in the intended way.

This can and does happen for a variety of reasons but in the case of Scottish renewables projects tends to be when there is a large amount of wind power being produced and not very much demand, or when there is an issue with the transmission system which means electricity cannot be shipped to where it is needed.

Constraint payments generate repeated headlines in those parts of the press that like to bash wind: 'Energy consumers paid £173m last year to turn windfarms off' was *The Telegraph* screamer in August 2019. The body of the article, to be fair, points out that the cost of balancing the system is just £6 per annum on the average consumer bill, and that not all of that spending is connected to spinning down wind.

It should be further noted that decisions on constraints are taken by the operator, not the wind farms, and are based on existing contractual arrangements with project owners, which essentially outline their buyout price and conditions well ahead of time. The matrix of factors to consider include weather conditions, level of consumer demand, any outages (planned or otherwise) across the network, and inputs from all generation segments as well as across interconnectors.

That has little traction for wind's opponents, it has to be said, and by extension feeds those related grievances against any expansion of the network that facilitates the sector's ongoing contribution to the energy mix.

However, cross the Minch to Lewis in the Outer Hebrides, navigate the Pentland Firth to Orkney, or beyond across the North Sea to Shetland, and there are many crying out for a modern, reliable grid network that offers increased and robust local services as well as a connection to the wider UK and international electricity markets.

But that should come as no surprise; everything is different on the islands.

MYTH 6

Wind requires additional back-up

Individual wind projects produce power at least 80 per cent of the time and in Scotland the sector has an average load factor of 30–50 per cent, depending on the site. Output is forecastable, which means that on still days power production can be brought into play from elsewhere on the electricity network.

Wind does not require more 'back-up' than any other technology. For comparison, low carbon rival, nuclear, features a load factor of around 70 per cent due to shutdowns for inspections, maintenance, unplanned outages and refuelling – and by the way, wind does not require any fuel.

8

Islands

THE COMMUNITY FOCUS and hippie ethos of the original wind pioneers in Scotland survived largely intact on Orkney, even through the extremes of the RO building boom. It was more by accident than design.

Veteran wind developer and long-time islander Richard Gauld believes commercial development across the Northern Isles cluster was restricted mainly by a scattered and fragmented pattern of land ownership and settlement. There were few Highland-style clearances on Orkney, which in turn meant no sprawling estates emptied of their inhabitants. Instead there remains the pattern of dispersed townships that pre-dated a sheep-centric mainland, with houses located every 500 metres or so on any habitable land.

The buildings mingle with protected moorland landscapes, added Gauld, with the result that 'there are really no large areas far enough away for people to locate large-scale developments'.

For those few sites that might be carved out, he added, open vistas contributed to making the perception of visual intrusion from low lying areas more profound, which in turn made planning permission quite literally an uphill battle.

Orkney was nevertheless an important part of the Scottish wind story, largely due to the nearly unrivalled resource blowing in off the Atlantic.

In addition to the pioneering Costa Head turbine in the 1950s, the history of which served to introduce this book, the island group also hosted early prototypes of modern machines including a bulky, two-bladed, three-megawatt unit built by Wind Energy Group partners Taylor Woodrow, British Aerospace and GEC. The MS3, as it was called, 'tested the theory' of island wind – as Gauld described it – and was itself a follow-on from a smaller prototype machine and ran between 1987 and 1997 at Burgar Hill in the north of the Orkney mainland before being pulled down in 2000. The design eventually produced a machine brought to market by a company in New Zealand.

Further test units also featured at the same location, largely built by European manufacturers in order to trial new models and technologies in very high wind-speed conditions. They still spin today.

A quick aside: Scotland also plays host to a similar but much more compact turbine test facility at Myers Hill outside Glasgow, established as part of efforts by the National Engineering Laboratory to explore different ways to ensure security of supply. Small machines were put through their paces but the initiative came up against what some in the wind industry considered 'the widespread de-industrialisation of the UK economy' in the 1980s. Manufacturing was the antithesis of the modern service economy that the government of the day was trying to create, according to some of those involved, so the work at Myers Hill was always fighting against the current. (The facility is now dwarfed by Scottish Power's nearby 539-megawatt Whitelee project, tapping the same winds. Apropos of nothing.)

The test programme on Orkney, in contrast to the important but less powerful results from its cousin on the mainland, had a profound impact on the islands. 'Because of these older projects, people weren't afraid of what wind was,' said Gauld. 'The people understood the technology and what it could offer. Once the first one went up others said, we can do that. It was almost the fact you could observe the technology and know what was possible that led to increased deployment.'

New horizons: Burgar Hill in Orkney played host to a number of experimental turbines.

Farmers in particular embraced turbine technology with single turbine deployments, while a number of limited-scale arrays were established often to the direct benefit of the surrounding communities. Local contractors learned how to build projects; island-based developers like Gauld's Orkney Sustainable Energy accumulated expertise; the electricity operator for the archipelago evolved management practices that balanced the requirements of the local network, home-grown Orkney generation, and the outlet offered by a limited-capacity wire to the mainland first established in 1982. Wind thrived at a small, almost intimate scale; it was widely seen as a natural part of existence.

The close relationship between power production on Orkney and the everyday lives of residents led to much of what followed in terms of the island's renewables revolution, widely chronicled elsewhere and globally renowned: early stage wave and tidal power, grid network innovations, hydrogen production for heat and transport, and wind all stitched together in a low-carbon smorgasbord. It is the realisation, on a very limited scale, of what is possible on a much larger stage – one shaped like Scotland, perhaps? – from an energy system heavily reliant on green energy.

It should be noted that Orkney has also played host to commercial development, albeit to a modest extent. Edinburgh company Hoolan Energy is the latest to join the fray and currently preparing to build the four-turbine Costa Head (yes, at that Costa Head) and the five-turbine Hesta Head projects by 2024.

The projects secured a government-backed contract in 2019 at a price of £39.65 per megawatt-hour under the so-called remote (read island) wind segment of the Contracts for Difference auctions. The category was established in 2018 following long-time lobbying by largely Scottish interests in recognition of the particular circumstances found in the islands, be those economic, technological or social.

To the north, meanwhile, Shetland features its own version of the Scottish wind narrative.

Turbine ambitions of all stripes – be those experimental, agricultural, community or commercial – were constrained on Shetland by an islands-only grid network operating completely independent of the mainland some 170km distant. The limited flexibility offered by Orkney's wire to shore was unavailable; system engineers during the early years of the UK wind boom were therefore very reluctant to inject renewables into the island energy mix and, when finally forced to act by a bit of political arm-twisting, limited the initial grid access to three smallish turbines at Burradale totalling just two megawatts.

The islands themselves were not anti-wind, as such. Small-scale domestic machines were very popular with a particular emphasis on wind-to-heat applications, of which large numbers were installed through the mid-2000s to convert breeze into warmth across village halls and other community assets across Shetland. There was simply no technical way, according to the network engineers, to meet the demands of multiple large-scale projects.

That said, following an initial period during which Burradale provided the grid operator with a degree of comfort based on real-life experience, the trio of machines at Shetland Aerogenerator's wind farm were permitted to expand with a pair of more powerful turbines. That state of play would remain the case until 2014 and the introduction of an active management system on the Shetland grid, essentially a series of smart controls and protocols that increased the capacity and robustness of the existing wires. The upgrade provided additional but still limited flexibility and allowed for a small amount of new wind power as well as other renewables including tidal.

The rate of progress was not enough for those watching the wind revolution take root across the Scottish mainland. Shetland had unquestioned resources, perhaps some of the best anywhere in the world, but it required a link with markets to the south, across the North Sea, if development of any scale was to progress. The idea of an interconnector was floated in the wake of Burradale's success. In the mid-2000s, initial approaches were made for a grid connection serving a project that would eventually become known as the Viking wind farm. Officials at Shetland Council alongside Shetland Aerogenerators veterans and other local interests believed there was potential in a project on local authority landholdings; they quickly realised they were not the only ones interested in wind on the islands.

Big companies from the UK and Europe had reached conclusions similar to those of the locals, and many had started to put pins in the same areas of the map already earmarked by the local authority and partners. Shetland Council recognised the benefits of teaming up with the undoubted muscle of what were heavy-hitting corporates, while still retaining control of development, and held what one islander called a 'beauty parade'. Perth utility SSE became an equal partner in the project.

Two prerequisites governed the design stage, both of which were addressed by size: the first was to justify the roughly £700 million investment in a subsea connection with the mainland through which power could be exported. UK energy regulator Ofgem is responsible for ensuring that money spent on the national grid network is affordable, justifiable and necessary; permission would not be forthcoming for anything less than a utility-scale project.

Just as importantly, the wind farm would need to provide a significant new revenue stream across a community that had grown accustomed to the cash payments linked to development and operation of the Sullom Voe oil terminal, payments which expired towards the end of the 1990s having established a fund estimated to be worth roughly £400 million. A large wind farm would do the trick. A very large wind farm.

Viking emerged into the glare of scrutiny in 2009 and was consented by ministers in 2012 as a 103-turbine array before surviving a legal challenge that ran through 2015; when or if finally built, it is likely to be somewhere around 450 megawatts. Corporate partner SSE struck a deal in 2019 to take control of the development on which construction started in 2020. Shetland, through its once council-run but now arm's-length charitable trust, retains a direct share in the profits of the wind farm but will also benefit financially from the usual lease payments, rates and economic knock-ons etc.

A number of other projects are also progressing across Shetland, some purely commercial, some driven by local interests, but none as large as Viking. All are of course designed to piggyback on a shiny new grid connection with the mainland, which at time of writing may still be some way away.

Viking and other Shetland hopefuls failed, despite widespread expectations of success, to secure a contract in the UK government's CfD auction in September 2019. SSE is nevertheless progressing on the basis that the wind farm will make a significant contribution to national net-zero ambitions while simultaneously boosting security of supply on the islands as well as local employment and economic benefit.

The history of Western Isles wind, meanwhile, falls somewhere between its northern counterparts, having both a strong community ethos running through its existing fleet and a series of large-scale commercial propositions looking to make an impact on the national scene.

Like Shetland, proposals for a large-scale interconnector to the mainland require the commitment of a substantial amount of generation capacity. And like Orkney, a constrained existing electricity link via Skye has allowed for existing development opportunities of single machines and small arrays.

That could have changed dramatically with the government contracts awarded last year to two developments on Lewis, EDF's 45-turbine Muaitheabhal project in the Pairc area in the

MYTH 7

Wind power does not reduce emissions

The carbon intensity of generation in Scotland –
ie the amount of CO_2 produced by creating electricity in the
country – has dropped dramatically since the beginning of the
commercial wind era, from more than 300g per kilowatt-hour
to around 50g. During that period, the energy mix features
less traditional generation but more renewables. Hard to
justify any other conclusion: wind power cuts emissions.

Making hay: some of the most productive wind turbines anywhere in the world are located in Orkney.

south of the island and BayWa's Druim Leathann at the top end of the Outer Hebrides, which will feature 14 turbines. Both are due to be completed in 2024 and will sell power at roughly £40 per megawatt-hour.

The projects have not at this stage, however, triggered the necessary approvals by regulator Ofgem for construction of a substantial subsea cable between Little Loch Broom on the mainland and the Arnish peninsula on Lewis, which would have eventually opened the door to further generation from other proposed wind farms both commercial and community. Revised proposals for the connection are expected be developed by network provider SSEN in a bid to find a way forward.

Muaitheabhal was originally developed by Eishken Estate owner and millionaire businessman Nicholas Oppenheim, who divides his time between the Lewis base, a London outpost and overseas commitments. He defied the expectations of the mainstream wind sector by securing consent for the initial phase of his independently developed wind farm in 2010 before selling the project to French company GDF (now known as Engie) in 2012. The around 190-megawatt plan, in an area remote even by Outer Hebridean standards, eventually passed into the control of utility EDF in 2016.

The latter company's similarly sized Stornoway project in the north of the island was widely seen as a frontrunner for the CfD auction in 2019 but failed to place. Proposed turbines on land controlled by the Stornoway Trust evolved from a controversial and much larger project, the Lewis wind farm, which was refused permission in 2008.

Arguments were put forward at that time, not just by the developer but by the local authority and the trust, about positive socio-economic benefits including justification for the transmission interconnector and an injection of manufacturing employment at the Arnish yard. However, nearly 11,000 objections were lodged against what was a 700 megawatt array on the basis of the perceived visual, landscape and ornithology impacts. Ministers eventually ruled that any pluses were outweighed by environmental minuses.

The opposition to wind in general, and the follow-on Stornoway plans specifically, appears to have become less vociferous in the ten years since the Lewis plans were knocked back. Perhaps it is because the latest generation of projects have much smaller footprints, perhaps it reflects a change in attitudes about wind power among an island population increasingly at home with the technology, perhaps the balance has shifted between the perceived social costs of the development and rewards including a transmission link to the mainland. It could be a little bit of all three.

Which is not to say everyone was happy about the Stornoway project. Significant dissent was voiced by rival community-based projects assisted by the Point and Sandwick

Trust, which wanted to replace roughly half of the EDF plans with four grassroots wind farms, retaining control and profits on the islands. They have to date been unsuccessful, although failure of the commercial version of the larger development to secure a government contract may re-open the door.

It is impossible to predict with any certainty where the island story will go next, although with the unquestioned resource and an ongoing appetite at both community and commercial scale there can be little doubt development will continue at pace. Some friction is inevitable as local ambitions and national-scale opportunities clash, although given the latter are necessary to justify investment in the sorts of crucial island transmission links that will facilitate the former, a mutually-beneficial approach may be the best way forward.

Viking is currently carrying that flag, and could potentially pave the way for all that follows on the islands. The behemoth of a project is also, as we move this history forward, as close as the land-based sector gets to the biggest of all big renewables hitters: offshore wind.

The quality of resource, volume of power and economies of scale that can be achieved by putting turbines at sea are immense. It is an advantage won over many years of trial and error, deployment and painful lessons, and can in part be traced back to a pioneering demonstration project in the Moray Firth.

Time to hit the water.

9

Wind Walks on Water

WHILE ONSHORE WIND boomed in Scotland through the 2000s, its offshore counterpart got off to a relatively slow start. It was, however, an innovative debut.

'What we achieved (in 2006–7) was eventually taken onwards by many others in offshore, although most seem unaware the Beatrice demonstrator was behind that,' said Dietmar Gosch. 'A lot of the work we carried out at that time provided experience for what came later across Europe,' he added of the two-turbine installation in the Moray Firth off north-east Scotland. 'It was pioneering.'

The open, amiable German earned a degree in applied physics from the University of Lubeck and also studied marketing management in Cape Town University before joining the wind industry in summer 2000. He displays a sincerity of belief in renewable energy that extends towards organised green politics in his home country. A serious man, Gosch is nevertheless quick to laugh, even at his own expense.

'We finalised the pre-assembly of the first nacelles for Beatrice in a car park in Bremerhaven port that until just a few weeks before had been used for storing second-hand cars destined for export to West Africa. The turbine components were so heavy they sunk almost 20 centimetres into the tarmac. And then one even hit the side of the ship while it was being loaded by a crane operator.' He shook his head in equal parts good humour and disbelief at the steepness of the learning curve. 'No serious damage done.'

On the job: Dietmar Gosch atop the Beatrice demonstration turbine in the Moray Firth, with the Beatrice oil platform in the background. The pioneering project was the first deep-water wind farm anywhere in the world and featured a number of industry innovations.
Courtesy of Dietmar Gosch

Gosch started his professional life in the German onshore wind market with since-defunct manufacturer DeWind before shifting into the international offshore sphere in 2003 as part of a turbine company at that time called Repower, later rebranded under new ownership as Senvion. 'They had decided offshore would be a growing part of their business and of the wind sector in general,' he said. 'They were probably a bit naive about what they and the rest of us were facing. Offshore turned out to be a seriously different business.'

How different?

For starters, it can be many times more expensive to build turbines in the water on a per-megawatt-installed basis, although there is more of a payback because of a stronger and more consistent and dependable wind resource (ie the breeze generally blows more often, in a less turbulent fashion, and arguably in a more forecast-able way). A large number of specialist contractors are required to build the project rather than the handful needed to complete a similar project onshore, and power must travel much farther across dedicated subsea and nearshore infrastructure to export into existing onshore grid networks and so consumers.

In a regulatory sense, there are often competitive auctions and/or lease payments to secure the rights to use publicly-held areas of the ocean, there is sometimes a higher bar for environmental impacts studies and, because of that, a much larger risk profile during the application stage. Technology in the early years was also unproven with the industry learning as it went along: high-profile failures, lengthy delays and very public embarrassment dogged many installations through the 2000s.

Finance was also a marked departure from onshore. Investments in the billions of pounds or euros, rather than the tens or even hundreds of millions necessary on land, required a range of innovative lenders alongside state export banks and other public cash. Partly because of that, offshore subsidies and supports were initially much more lucrative than their onshore wind equivalents, largely in a bid to make the industry attractive to early adopters and to support the learning curve necessary to produce the utility-scale volumes of carbon-free electricity that would eventually be pulled from the North, Irish and Baltic seas.

In Scotland, the Beatrice demonstrator was conceived as the wider offshore industry was establishing a shallow water, close to shore track record that was starting to irk some of those with houses on the coastline or with holidays booked at the seaside. Deployment in the Moray Firth would form part of efforts to address what could be called the eyesore problem, under the guise of the EU-supported DOWNVIND programme. Every international industry collaboration requires an acronym, which in this case – and ignoring some obvious problems of abbreviatory consistency – stood for Distant Offshore Windfarms with No Visual Impact in Deepwater.

Hydrocarbons company Talisman and utility SSE were the main drivers, the former under the dogged determination of long-time Aberdeen oil and gas man Allan MacAskill. His concept was to build turbines alongside the existing Beatrice A offshore platform to help power operations at the oil field, thereby lowering the cost of production. It would also lower the pricetag of the demo, he said at the time: 'It gives us the opportunity to test-drive this technology at a lower cost than available elsewhere.'

Total spending for the experiment was expected to be €30 million with the EU part-funding the exercise via a cheque of around €6 million and Westminster and Holyrood providing a further €3 million each. The consortium included 14 partners from across a range of countries including Sweden, Spain, France, Netherlands and Germany.

Dietmar Gosch saw Beatrice as an opportunity to showcase Repower's market-leading but early-stage 5M turbine, which had been developed in-house with a focus on reliability and serviceability. 'You have to go big if you are going to be a serious player in this market, we said at the time,' remembered the German. 'It may have been a bold move but it was the right thing to do.'

The model, which as the name hints had a capacity of five megawatts, was nearly twice as powerful as its main rivals. It was also one of the first designs produced specifically for life above the waves; the majority of the operational offshore fleet at the time was composed of onshore machines adapted to life on the water, known as 'marinised'. MacAskill was convinced by the German company's pitch, which was based on an unflinching confidence in the Repower technology despite there being just a single prototype machine installed onshore in its home country. The deal to supply two units to Beatrice was signed in summer 2005.

A German crew of around 20 took up residence in the Scottish Highlands for construction of the demonstrator. Some shared a house near the project's Nigg base while others found rooms in a hotel in nearby Tain. Downtime was spent at a local Indian restaurant and the occasional trip to the pub or, in what was an unusually sunny summer in 2006, at the beach. 'There was a true sense of team spirit among the Germans, the Scots and the rest,' said Gosch. 'It was really a pioneering mood.'

A number of important firsts were achieved. The turbines were assembled in their entirety on the quayside at the Nigg yard – including towers fabricated by the short-lived Camcal at the Arnish yard on the island of Lewis – ahead of installation as complete units near the Beatrice platform. Belgian specialist heavylift ship *Rambiz*, which had a long shear-leg crane on its hull, transported the fully-assembled 900-tonne machines to the demo site roughly 25km from shore. Still supported by the hooks of the crane, much like a large man carrying an over-sized lantern as he walked down a dark passage, the turbines were then lifted into place atop jacket foundations.

The latter were four-legged, lattice-work substructures more commonly used in the oil and gas industry. They allowed the

MYTH 8

Wind turbines kill huge numbers of birds

Nobody likes to see wildlife paying the price for human development. However it must be remembered that domestic cats kill something in the region of 10,000 times more birds than wind turbines, and our feathered friends fly fatally into radio or mobile phone mast, 18 times more often as they do into wind farms. Specifically in the realm of energy, according to a Danish study, wind is linked to 0.27 bird deaths per gigawatt-hour of electricity produced, while fossil fuel plants are responsible for 19 times that total, or 5.18 bird deaths per gigawatt-hour. Offshore wind posts even lower rates of bird fatalities due to behaviour including much higher or lower flight paths.

turbines to sit in waters some 45 metres deep, around twice the industry standard and well beyond what was considered possible using established wind sector technologies. Fife company Bifab built the structures at its yard in Methil under a contract worth £5 million; designs for the jackets were from Norwegian engineering outfit OWEC.

The first turbine was put in place in the Moray Firth in summer 2006 but bad weather in autumn of that year, as well as rival contractual obligations for Rambiz, forced the second Repower machine to wait out the winter in Nigg. It was eventually installed offshore in spring 2007 and, following final commissioning, supplied regular power to the Beatrice oil operations. 'I think next to the smaller Danish turbines going into the water (in the early 1990s), the Beatrice demo gave the next huge kick to offshore wind,' said Gosch.

Lessons learned, particularly about jackets and very large turbines, would be commercially deployed by 2010 off England, then off Germany and, some years later, would make a return to Scottish waters as part of a much wider uptake by the industry. That homecoming would start, as anyone with an interest in high-profile ding-dongs may recall, with another demonstration project, known as the European Offshore Wind Deployment Centre, just north of the UK's oil and gas capital.

The innovative project was originally championed by the Aberdeen Renewable Energy Group and taken into construction in 2016 by Swedish utility and AREG member Vattenfall. It features 11 giant turbines on jacket foundations, albeit attached to the seafloor via a suction technology rather than with piles. It is most famous, of course, for being relatively close to President Donald Trump's golf course development at Menie.

An entire book could be devoted to the very public rammy that followed – on interwoven fronts – which sucked in area residents, protestors, conservationists, the local authority, the Scottish government, then First Minister Alex Salmond, Trumpian views on the myriad evils of wind power, documentary film makers and repeated legal challenges to planning permission. Concerns about the rights and wrongs of the golf course became entangled in the wind war, as did the balance between commercial concerns and the environment. There was even a separate court case and counter-claim centred on peeing in the outdoors, just to indicate how fractious it all became. Rows resulted in repeated delays to the wind farm planned for the waters off Blackdog, a project which had originally been proposed in 2003 as a line of 20 turbines running parallel to shore for 8km. Power from the demonstrator was finally exported to the grid in 2018. Trump continues to develop his golf complex.

On the commercial side of the Scottish offshore equation, meanwhile, activity officially started as long ago as 2007 while Aberdeen was still becalmed and the Beatrice demo was in the final stages of being completed. The comparatively 'old school' Robin Rigg project was composed of east and west sections of 90 megawatts each off the coast of Dumfries and Galloway, although to be frank it was not a particularly Scottish affair.

There was little to distinguish the array from English and Welsh counterparts of a similar vintage, beyond its physical location north of the maritime boundary in the Solway Firth and a bespoke planning process established by Holyrood to consent the project. It featured tried and tested technology in shallow water relatively close to shore, in line with nine very similar projects already up and running south of the border.

German utility developer E.ON led the project from its UK base in Coventry, set up an operations and maintenance base at Workington in Cumbria and exported power to the national grid via a substation near Carlisle.

Execution was both complicated and hampered by difficult seabed conditions in the Solway, which features a sandy bottom prone to shifting beneath strong tides and currents. A timetable that originally scheduled full operations in mid-2009 was eventually completed in spring 2010. The difficult conditions subsequently dictated premature decommissioning of two of 60 of the project's turbines. Units A1 and B1 fell victim in 2015 to what E.ON described as 'natural movements of the sandbank and the loss of seabed level' in the northern section of the project. Operations at the rest of the project continue largely as normal.

The country's second commercial offshore project was completed in 2019 in what amounted to something of a homecoming in the Moray Firth. UK utility SSE, Danish investor Copenhagen Infrastructure Partners and Chinese company Red Rock Power built the Beatrice wind farm in the waters north of the original demo of the same name starting in 2016. A route to market was secured via a government-awarded contract at an index-linked price of £140 per megawatt-hour for 15 years.

The £2 billion array represents an evolution, some 13 years later, of what was the early-stage 'phase two' plan for Beatrice championed by MacAskill for Talisman and SSE. It features jacket foundations and 84 large turbines in deep waters. A neighbouring project, Moray East, is due for completion in 2021 and can also be linked back to the initial Talisman outline and technology solutions; it will feature 100 turbines on jacket foundations in the same broad area of water.

Power produced at Moray will receive government-guaranteed, index-linked payments of £57.50 per megawatt-hour for 15 years, an indication of both the increased level of competition for offshore wind contracts but also the speed at which the costs of the technology have come down over a very short period of time.

The Moray Firth projects feature more powerful turbines from different manufacturers, while whole-turbine installations were not included at either of the commercial descendants of the Beatrice demo, or in any widespread way elsewhere in the industry. 'We tested the concept successfully but the disadvantages ended up outweighing the advantages,' said Gosch. 'Installation of separate elements became the norm, with weather windows being the key factor in their favour. Transport times from shore, in particular, were an issue with the whole-turbine approach.'

One exception was Hywind Scotland, another pioneering project but this time for floating offshore wind.

Norwegian oil and gas company Equinor selected the waters off Peterhead in the north-east of the country for deployment of five turbines on spar buoy foundations moored to the seafloor. The energy department at Holyrood promised any successful installation before October 2018 a premium on the usual RO payments, both to attract the new sector to Scottish waters and, ostensibly, to encourage investment in local manufacturing supply chains.

Equinor largely sidestepped the latter but, in what was a straight fight with a rival project site off the US state of Maine, was tempted enough by the millions of pounds of extra state supports on offer to choose the Buchan Deep off Aberdeenshire for what was the second demonstration of its Hywind floating technology. A single, smaller prototype had been installed in 2009 off the island of Karmoy on the west coast of Norway; its successor would feature five machines each more than twice as powerful.

The completed turbine/substructure units off Scotland weighed in at 11,200 tonnes each, stretched to 175 metres above the water and were tethered to the seafloor in some 105 metres of water with a trio of chains connected to suction anchors. The floating spars are 14.4 metres in diameter at the base and feature a draught of 78 metres; water and solid ballast keep the components upright in the water. The array was the first of its kind anywhere in the world and represented a significant step on the path towards commercialisation of the technology.

Echoes of the original Beatrice demo can be found in the early stages of the project, when giant semi-submersible heavylift vessel *Saipem S7000* mated complete Siemens Gamesa

Lessons learned: many of the advances deployed at the Beatrice
demonstration project were subsequently adopted by the offshore
wind industry.
Courtesy of Dietmar Gosch

turbines to the spar foundation using dual cranes and a
'proprietary stability frame'. The operation was carried out in
the deep waters off Stord on the west coast of Norway before
each unit was towed across the North Sea for deployment in
the Buchan Deep.

Scotland's second floating demonstration project is installed
nearby at the Dog Hole off Stonehaven. The Kincardine project
was created by Pilot Offshore, which was founded by none other
than Beatrice mainstay Allan MacAskill in partnership with
former Scottish energy minister and sometime onshore renewables
developer Nicol Stephen. The initiative was eventually taken over
by Spanish company ACS Cobra and construction of the multi-
phase 50 megawatt wind farm is due to complete in 2020.

Other projects are on the horizon. French company EDF is

preparing to build the Neart na Gaoithe project in the outer Firth of Forth while SSE is progressing plans for its Seagreen project in the outer Firth of Tay, which secured a contract with the UK government in September 2019 at the remarkably low price of £41 per megawatt-hour. Crown Estate Scotland, which manages the seabed in the public interest, is also in the midst of a new licensing round for the country's waters that could result in new development and further additions to the portfolio, assuming planning permission is secured and a route to market can be secured.

It is unclear what the ultimate balance between onshore and offshore will be in Scotland, where installations on the water have a long way to go to catch up with the number of projects already established on land. The hiatus in the earthbound sector created an opportunity for a significant comeback from the offshore crowd north of the border but the same challenges – access to grid, aviation conflicts, supply chain concerns, costs – are likely to slow the overall pace and eat into what might otherwise be possible in terms of appetite for deployment. Industry veteran Ray Hunter believes the country will in time work towards a 50:50 split between the two technologies: 'There is just so much opportunity offshore,' he pointed out.

The Beatrice demo is meanwhile preparing to come full circle. The oil field hosting the project has been shut down and is slated to be decommissioned, including the two Repower machines, between 2024 and the end of 2027.

Consideration was given to keeping the wind turbines. However, as current field operator Repsol Sinopec indicated in end-of-life plans submitted to the UK government, retention as part of the commercial and nearby Beatrice project was ruled out after 'the partners in that development cited the obsolete design and the associated high maintenance burden as a reason to exclude the two existing turbines'. A community-funded option was also investigated, according to the oil company:

Although the wind turbines were considered suitable for reuse individually, the project stalled due to commercial and shareholder requirements. There was also the additional complexity that there is currently no grid connection from the Beatrice wind turbines. The costs associated with this grid connection were prohibitive.

The Ministry of Defence also considered using the installations as part of military training but this too was eventually deemed surplus to requirements.

Decommissioning will entail 'reverse installation' of the turbines and jacket substructures, although the exact methodology will depend on the results of a commercial tender closer to the deadline later this decade. Once brought to shore, the materials will be recycled to the greatest extent possible, 'unless alternative options are identified to be viable and more appropriate'.

The waters around the iconic turbines, which on a clear day can be seen from the hilltops around the Moray Firth, will soon be returned to the natural wave-state of pre-development. The legacy of Beatrice will, however, be long reflected in the 184 giant machines spinning elsewhere off northern Scotland, the established European fleet of megascale turbines on jacket foundations and the exponential global rise in deep-water projects.

'Not everything went exactly as planned or intended,' said Gosch. 'But we got there.'

Given what would happen to the once booming onshore sector, it was just as well.

Second Intermission

REPORTING ON THE renewable energy sector in the 2010s became an ever-increasing battle against a rising tide of corporatism, control freakery and paranoia.

As the industry joined the economic big leagues, growing numbers of people in positions of responsibility began to hide beneath their metaphorical desks in the sincere belief that information was best shared rarely, only through narrow official channels and, when necessary, false either by omission or misdirection. The wind business had grown up, installed a lot of projects, made money, assumed a high profile on the national stage – particularly after large-scale offshore deployment raised stakes into the billions rather than millions – and as a result was more concerned about managing its public image.

The widely-held perception among the general population that wind was all about being green and fuzzy no longer applied by default. In the mainstream media and national level politics, probing – if sometimes irrelevant or even calculatingly detrimental – questions, designed to damage through the asking, whatever the answer, were repeatedly being raised about costs, about environmental impacts, about the balance between more expensive consumer bills ('how high?' the self-appointed defenders of the public yelled) and reductions in carbon ('how little?' wailed the same). On the stage of national opinion, every fact was a battleground, every achievement a question mark, every setback a doomsday.

Hiding from the glare of publicity was in part understandable; the renewables industry had only done what government policy had encouraged it to do – build wind farms – but was nevertheless under assault from powerful, entrenched interests including some of the traditional generators, climate change deniers, countryside nostalgia-philes and sometimes rabid anti-green elements.

Against that background, an independent-minded reporter determined to cover the good, bad and ugly of the industry was in the first instance fine but in the second and third anything but welcome. Sources dried up, particularly in the utilities and larger companies, as three-line whips were imposed under penalty of career and all inquiries channelled through press offices. Fresh-recruit PRs that neither understood journalism nor the renewables business regurgitated pre-prepared responses designed to appease a right-leaning national press pack scrabbling for scandal in an increasingly politicised environment. Actual information was minimal. Follow-up questions, clarifications or requests for further detail were ignored.

An omertà was enforced that sealed off the usual and long-standing routes of communication; rebels, hippies, candid individualists and old-school PRs muzzled, moved on, bundled into the soundproofed trunks of limos and dumped in the East River (okay, not that last bit). News gathering went deep underground; my readers needed to get the information they were paying for and no excuses. Increasing numbers of stories produced angry calls from heads of communication, marketing chiefs and paid-gun agencies not because they were wrong but because they bypassed the official machinery. The front page exclusives kept coming, a thousand witch hunts for 'the source' were launched.

The siege mentality was of course ultimately counter-productive: the tighter the wind industry tried to strangle information the more 'bad news' seeped pungently into the market. Small problems became magnified due to the lack of any high-level context, struggles were all the more sexy for being denied, real issues of import that deserved wider discussion became hushed, unconfirmed secrets discussed in stage whispers out of the public eye.

In an attempt to better control the narrative, some press and/or marketing offices – the roles increasingly blurred – began to form close relationships with publications boasting loose editorial standards and weak balance sheets. 'Placed' stories became distressingly acceptable; information was presented without scrutiny and often unethically close to related commercial materials. Everything was 'amazing', everything was 'groundbreaking', everything was 'great'; the wind industry was always 'fantastic'. Thought leadership, which 99 per cent of the time was a sales pitch masquerading as an opinion, became widespread. Everything that was wrong with an increasingly sick journalism in the modern, click-obsessed era found a happy home across a renewables sector desperate to tell what it claimed was only ever a good news story. Pollyanna, your table is ready.

The justification, even among some of those from the early days who should have known better, was that it was the way of the world, not a big deal, a means to an end – that it was naive to think otherwise. Wind power and the wider renewables sector, however, was supposed to be better, it wasn't meant to have that rotten smell of slick corporate dishonesty, that necessary evil of a million little lies, beneath a shiny green exterior.

Suddenly wind power – the revolution which I had inserted into the heart of my journalism, which I had dedicated many years of my life to covering, which was fundamentally important – wasn't about changing the world.

Suddenly renewables was just another business, stripped of its mystique and aura, reporting primarily to shareholders and big investors, increasingly distant from its activist roots.

Suddenly the day job was a repeated butting of heads with a cloistered and aloof money-making machine; increasingly it all seemed to be all about greed.

Suddenly it wasn't quite as much fun.

10

Daventry Pulls the Plug

ON THURSDAY 18 JUNE 2015, the conditions for generating electricity from wind power were excellent in most parts of Scotland. A steady breeze was blowing out of the west at between 12 and 16mph through most of the day, chasing away cloud cover and the occasional scattered shower. Skies had mostly cleared and the sun had yet to set as the clock approached 10.00pm, a hop, skip and jump away from the longest day of the year.

The collective mood of the onshore wind industry was dark by comparison.

Secretary of State for Energy and Climate Change Amber Rudd had earlier that day informed Westminster Parliament, via a written statement, that the UK 'had enough onshore wind' and as a result the RO regime would end a year earlier than originally scheduled in June 2016; future rounds of the government's CfD auction would, meanwhile, be closed to all mainland wind projects. The broad direction of the message was not completely unexpected as it was in line with Conservative manifesto commitments made in the Westminster election in May that year; however, the absoluteness and immediacy of the policy change, and its reach into the CfD regime, came as a brutal surprise.

With some exceptions.

Chris Heaton-Harris, a Conservative MP for Daventry in Northamptonshire and a vociferous onshore wind critic, may have been the happiest man in England. He entered Parliament

As Under-Secretary at the Department for Energy and Climate Change in 2015, Amber Rudd explains to the House of Commons that the UK had 'enough' onshore wind.
Screen grab with kind permission of www.parliamentlive.tv

in May 2010 having previously served as a member of the European Parliament for the East Midlands. Political office came on the heels of a career in the wholesale fruit and vegetable sector.

Judging by his official register of interests, he is a keen sports spectator (in addition to being a qualified football referee). NFL UK provided a hospitality ticket worth £479 to a gridiron game at the national stadium in Wembley in 2017, the English Premier League gifted three tickets to Chelsea v Watford and two tickets to Arsenal v Everton, both in 2015 and worth more than £1,200 combined. From Coca-Cola, he secured tickets and hospitality for himself and three family members at four events and the closing ceremony of the London Olympics in 2012 (value: £11,750).

A donation from Liberty OneSteel coincided with an inter-parliamentary cricket tournament in Australia in 2017. The company is somewhat ironically part of a corporate group currently working towards construction of onshore wind farms in Scotland; Indian billionaire businessman and Liberty Group boss Sanjeev Gupta appears not to hold a grudge, having donated a £1,865 helicopter transfer for the MP from Northamptonshire to a party in Yorkshire in 2016.

On entering Westminster, it did not take long for Heaton-Harris to raise the issue of renewables. His maiden speech, just some weeks after being elected, included a reference to the 'folly that is onshore wind energy', a position he had developed during his time as an MEP and despite being a self-confessed 'greenie' at the start of his political life.

The MP said from the government benches on 27 May 2010: 'Not only does (onshore wind) dramatically change the nature of the landscape for ever – and as we have very little beautiful English countryside left, so we should try to treasure the bit we have – but it does little to help us on our battle to reduce carbon emissions... Science is not on the side of this sort of wind power.'

In July 2010 he asked, in a question that did not apply in Scotland, whether proposals were forthcoming that would allow residents to 'prevent major planning proposals proceeding in their areas', adding the status quo was 'disempowering local communities' and was 'profoundly counterproductive'. In November of that year he moved an eventually unsuccessful motion to give communities 'a real say' by allowing local authorities in England and Wales to establish minimum setback distances for wind turbines, seen by many in the renewables business as a trojan horse policy designed to facilitate a de facto moratorium on new projects.

Heaton-Harris considered onshore wind 'as useful as a cat-flap on a submarine', and he was not alone. In January 2012, he penned a letter to then Prime Minister David Cameron, signed by 105 of his fellow MPs, raising concerns over the 'inefficient and intermittent energy production that typifies onshore wind'.

MYTH 9

Wind uses more carbon than it saves

The majority of wind farms in Scotland pay back all of the
carbon created during supply and construction of a project
within the first 12 months, while those built within some
particularly peat-heavy areas take a longer time but still
measured in years rather than decades. Deep peat, as an aside,
is avoided whenever and wherever possible not just because
it is a significant carbon sink, but because it is expensive and
complicated to build on.

The letter called on the government to 'dramatically cut the subsidies for onshore wind' and to spread the savings among 'reliable renewable energy production and energy efficiency measures'. It also called for changes to the planning system in England and Wales that would give local residents greater say over project decisions.

In October 2012, the MP took his opposition to the industry one step further by co-authoring the book *Together Against Wind: A Step By Step Guide to Opposing a Wind Farm in Your Area*.

Heaton-Harris continued to argue in Parliament and elsewhere that the planning process in England and Wales was unfair and that as a result people felt their views and wishes were being ignored. He said that as of 2011–2 there was already enough onshore wind to meet the UK's 2020 targets for that technology segment, and that the RO was set at too high a level, which was both driving over-development and creating fuel poverty due to the cost burden on consumers.

'I suggest that how the onshore wind industry has treated communities up and down this country has done untold damage to how people see renewables in total as part of our energy provision,' he said in a separate debate.

As the 2015 General Election approached, according to his own recollection, he was able to 'persuade, cajole, elbow, nudge and force my own political party' into changing how it approached wind in the planning system in England and Wales. Heaton-Harris also 'had enough of these people [the wind industry] and how they dealt with my constituents'. He therefore convinced Prime Minister David Cameron, by his own reckoning, 'to take on my well-registered and well-documented concerns and my ideas about how we should progress, and to state that there would be no new subsidies for onshore wind'.

The policy was included in the 2015 manifesto, although the wider context deserves a mention. The Conservatives were facing a significant ballot box challenge, largely in their English heartlands, from the far-right UK Independence Party, which in addition to its core remit of pulling the state out of the EU was also vehemently anti-renewables. Just as Cameron championed an in-out vote in a bid to head off his rivals to the right and to appease that wing of his own party so, many believe, did the Tories go 'all the way' with the 'no new onshore wind' promise.

Some in the renewables industry believe to this day that the Conservatives painted themselves into a corner with the manifesto without ever intending to honour the specific line about onshore. The party did not expect to win a majority, according to the theory, and so inserted the moratorium into its literature on a no-risk basis. The expectation was for the policy to be traded off as part of discussions to establish a repeat coalition with the Liberal Democrats, a party far more supportive of renewables. No one involved ever directly confirmed what has become a widely-accepted and still supported narrative within wind circles.

There is, as a related and timely aside, a very large overlap between the anti-Europe wing of the Conservatives and the anti-onshore wind element. Heaton-Harris was himself chair of arch-Leaver collective the European Research Group before being appointed as a parliamentary under-secretary at the Department for Exiting the European Union. He resigned that post on 3 April 2019 over delays to Brexit.

It should also be remembered that the Conservatives only had one MP in Scotland both before and after the 2015 vote, albeit the party jumped to 13 (of 59 total) following the snap General Election in 2017. The latter boost was largely down to the increasing polarisation in Scottish politics between unionists and nationalists following the 45:55 yes/no independence referendum in 2014, and arguably had little to do with renewables policy. Scotland, clearly, was caught up in a spat that had little significant traction outside of England.

The 2015 manifesto promise itself was relatively

straightforward, if open to questioning on some of the assertions presented as fact. It read:

> Onshore wind now makes a meaningful contribution to our energy mix and has been part of the necessary increase in renewable energy. Onshore wind farms often fail to win public support, however, and are unable by themselves to provide the firm capacity that a stable energy system requires. As a result, we will end any new public subsidy for them and change the law so that local people have the final say on wind farm applications.

The latter element, also put into effect on 18 June 2015, did not apply to Scotland where powers over planning are devolved. Changes to the RO subsidy system, however, were by this point completely outwith the control of Holyrood following what many north of the border considered a constitutional ambush, carried out in the House of Lords 18 months before. It was almost as if someone, somewhere, had a plan. Even then.

Amendment 54 had been adopted by peers in December 2013 as part of the wider Energy Bill then working its way through the Parliament under the Tory/LibDem coalition government. Scottish National Party energy spokesman Mike Weir, MP for Angus at the time, called the measure and the way it was put forward 'an outrageous example of the unionist parties ganging up to remove power from the Scottish Parliament. Worse still they did so by introducing last-minute amendments in the unelected House of Lords, rather than having the courage to debate it on the floor of the House of Commons.'

Weir pointed out in comments made in the House of Commons that there had been no consultation on the amendment with the Scottish government, led by the SNP, or with the Scottish Parliament. He said there was no 'reasonable explanation as to why this happened in such an underhand manner'. Weir added, against the background of the pending independence referendum:

> This is yet another example of Tories and Labour ganging up at Westminster against Scotland's interests... The reality is they are removing Scotland's existing powers by stealth.

The government countered from the dispatch box that it had every right to make the change and suggested that primary legislation introduced in the Lords was bringing change through the 'front door', rather than in an underhanded way. The amendment was adopted and passed as part of the wider Energy Bill, giving Westminster the power to shut down the RO across the UK at any time and without consultation with Holyrood.

Trade body Scottish Renewables said the onshore death knell, when it duly arrived courtesy of the written statement in June 2015, was 'neither fair nor reasonable'. The organisation put a potential pricetag of £3 billion on business that would be lost and then chief executive Niall Stuart called the decision 'bad for jobs, bad for investment'. He argued in a press release that it 'can only hinder Scotland and the UK's efforts to meet binding climate change targets'. SR predicted around two gigawatts of onshore wind across 250 Scottish projects, all developed to take advantage of the RO mechanism, would be left on the shelf as a result of the accelerated end-date.

Ruling the sector out of follow-on Contracts for Difference auctions also attracted brickbats from Stuart. 'Pushing onshore wind out of CfD altogether could see development almost completely grind to a halt,' he said. 'The competitive pressures of the CfD auction process have already driven down the costs of new onshore wind projects by around 15 per cent and continued allocation could potentially see wind competitive

Satisfied: Daventry MP Chris Heaton-Harris was a long-time opponent of onshore wind.
Screen grab with kind permission of www.parliamentlive.tv

with all new forms of generation by the end of this decade. It makes no sense to stop that progress, or to exclude the cheapest from of renewables deployable at scale from bidding in the next allocation round.'

The SNP, in a refrain oft-repeated following the September 2014 referendum, said the Conservatives had once again 'misled' Scottish voters. 'The Tory plans are a huge threat to the renewables industry in Scotland and represent a total betrayal towards people who were persuaded to vote No after being told that Scotland's renewables sector was only safe if Scots rejected independence,' Highland MSP Rob Gibson, a man with a constituency packed full of green energy reality and potential, said at the time in what were widely reported comments. 'Only nine months on, the UK government is pulling the plug on our burgeoning industry. The duplicity is totally unacceptable.'

Even government-produced analysis in London ran counter to the arguments for the manifesto promise. An 'attitude tracker' on energy issues first produced in July 2012 showed that 66 per cent of those surveyed across the UK either supported or strongly supported the onshore wind sector, with only 12 per cent either opposed or strongly opposed and 20 per cent being neutral. A total of 79 per cent of those questioned were supportive of renewables in general for providing electricity, fuel and heat.

Data also showed that 69 per cent of people believed the renewables industry provided economic benefit to the UK, 55 per cent said they would be happy to have 'a large-scale renewable energy development in my area', with 78 per cent saying projects 'should provide direct benefit to the communities in which they are located'. Figures produced ahead of the General Election in 2015 were little changed, albeit there had been some fluctuation – generally upwards and then back down – in the intervening years.

Directly corresponding figures on Scottish attitudes are not readily available but an unscientific scroll through a variety of similar surveys during the same period indicated that those living north of the border are broadly more supportive of the sector than elsewhere in the UK, not less. And of course Scottish government policy was overtly in favour of onshore wind.

First Minister Nicola Sturgeon wrote to Cameron in June 2015 to highlight the 'disproportionate impact' the new wind farm policy would have on Scotland, where '70 per cent of affected developments' would be located. She added: 'This comes despite the Scottish government's support for the onshore wind sector proving popular at successive elections, and your plans proving unpopular.'

The FM raised concerns over the impacts on investor confidence and called the move 'anti-business' while contrasting the policy with the aims of a crucial UN summit taking place in Paris later that year.

Your government's decision to cut planned support
for clean green renewable energy could not come

at a worse time given the forthcoming climate talks and shows a complete lack of leadership on climate change.

The move, she added, would make it more difficult for Scotland to meet its long-term targets for renewable energy.

All pleas fell on deaf ears and the onshore wind era in Scotland would soon enter a deep funk that is still being felt to this day.

Heaton-Harris, for the record, declined to provide additional details on how or whether Scotland and Scottish concerns informed his onshore wind campaign at Westminster. The door remains open to the elected parliamentarian for Daventry to contribute to any subsequent edition of this book.

Scottish Electricity Generation

2006

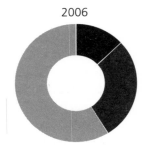

■ Renewables: 13.3%　　■ Nuclear: 27.1%　■ Fossil fuels: 57.3%

2010

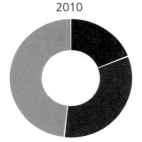

■ Renewables: 19.2%　　■ Nuclear: 30.9%　■ Fossil fuels: 48.4%

2018

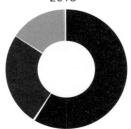

■ Renewables: 54.9%　　■ Nuclear: 28.2%　■ Fossil fuels: 15.7%

Source: Scottish Government Energy
Statistics Database (BEIS).

11

Becalmed

THE SCOTTISH ONSHORE wind sector has been in enforced super slowmo since 2018, showing few signs of life when compared in particular with the boom years that preceded the Westminster shutdown. However, the period of limbo, if nothing else, provides an opportunity to take a quick detour and – so many metaphors! – hit a for-once stationary target in terms of some important numbers. If stats leave you cold, feel free to skip ahead a few pages to resume the narrative.

Scotland currently hosts roughly 8,200 megawatts of onshore wind turbines, which in the most recent year produced somewhere around 17,000 gigawatt hours of electricity, according to official government data. Across all renewables technologies, including around 980 megawatts of offshore wind, the figure is more than 25,000 gigawatt-hours.

What does that represent? Scotland will in an average year generate between 45,000 and 50,000 gigawatt-hours of electricity per annum across all technologies – nuclear, gas, wind, other renewables etc – while consuming between 35,000 and 40,000 gigawatt-hours domestically. The remaining generation is exported with the majority going to England and Wales; a smaller amount crosses into Northern Ireland. Scotland also imports a small amount of power each year during certain market conditions, generally less than 1,400 gigawatt-hours.

In percentage terms, and as of the most recent full year measured (2018), onshore wind in Scotland provides around

34 per cent of all generation and 42 per cent of the amount of electricity used domestically. That is not a peak nor based on overall capacity; it doesn't represent just one good day, the percentage is derived directly from generation as measured across a 12-month period. The combined renewable fleet including offshore wind, where the newest projects have yet to inform statistics, supplies 55 per cent of all generation and somewhere around 75 per cent of the level of power used just in Scotland, albeit more on some days than on others. England and Wales, for comparison, generate a combined 280 gigawatt-hours per annum with renewables – including a much bigger offshore wind fleet – contributing 71 gigawatt-hours, or around 25 per cent of electricity.

Limited newbuild generation has been added since those official figures were last compiled, but it is safe to assume that as the amount of power used declines in the short term – through efficiencies, a reduction in power-hungry industries and other savings – the percentage provided by wind in that up to 50,000 gigawatt-hour per annum total will have gone up, even if only by a relatively small amount.

There was a rush of construction following the tolling of the bell in Westminster in June 2015 as projects raced towards the various accelerated RO cut-off dates, then a final hurrah as the remaining obligation wind farms crossed the finish line in 2018 courtesy of a range of exemptions. More than two-thirds of the 350 megawatt total in that final year was a single project in the Highlands, SSE's 228-megawatt Stronelairg near Loch Ness.

The ten Contracts for Difference winners, selected following the original auctions in 2014, were due online between 2017 and 2019 but in some cases, and with shades of the 1990s-era imbalance between project readiness and bidding strategies returning to haunt the industry, construction timetables proved to be overly optimistic.

Even with efforts to push the stragglers over the line,

Rare breed: the shift from the Renewables Obligation to the Contracts for Difference regime resulted in a dramatic drop in wind farm construction in Scotland, with projects like Tom nan Clach in the Highlands now the exception rather than the rule.
With kind permission of Infinergy Ltd

adjustment among the industry to the reality of what quickly became known as the 'post-subsidy' regime came quickly and was brutal. Development offices in Edinburgh and Glasgow were shuttered, portfolios offloaded, projects abandoned, companies sold or dissolved. Many working at the sharp end of onshore wind shifted to other industries, some left the country, others tried to ride through the doldrums. Contractors and the supply chain adopted revised strategies, career plans were redrawn.

Jobs in the onshore sector north of the border declined by 29 per cent from 2016 to 2017, according to figures from industry body Scottish Renewables. It is widely accepted, while not yet statistically supported, that many more have joined the 2,000-plus who lost their posts in the immediate aftermath of the onshore wind moratorium.

An industry conference held in Liverpool in autumn of 2015 previewed the downturn to come. Many stalls were empty, the exhibitors having already pulled out of the sector or simply opting to save money by not showing up. The aisles of the cavernous ACC exhibition hall on the Kings Dock were at times all but empty and tumbleweeds would not have been out of place; among the sparse collection of delegates in attendance there was gloom and doom. Many were polishing CVs, talking about a move into offshore, or wave and tidal, or back to oil and gas, or relocating to Ireland, the US, Canada. There was plenty of drinking going on, at a much earlier hour than usual.

Others took a different, more optimistic approach. A handful of independent developers and suppliers were convinced that some Scottish onshore wind could prosper in the new era, based on a revised business model and on a purely market basis, ie without government intervention of any kind.

The first step would be to maximise the chance of success. This would mean turning away from any potential site that fell short of excellent on either wind speed or quality; it also ruled out any project that faced significant constraints in terms of planning, grid connections, radar impacts, noise or wildlife. Development is expensive and sites likely to require more time and energy than absolutely necessary to secure consent were instantly rendered obsolete.

The second key was size: post-subsidy projects would ideally be 50 megawatts and above to take advantage of economies of scale during both procurement and construction. Many hopefuls are now much, much larger with a series of 'supermega' projects of 300 megawatts and up entering the planning system over the period 2017–9.

Finally, turbines needed to be bigger, both in height and span, in order to boost capacity and, more importantly, yield. Generally speaking, the higher you are above an onshore site, the stronger and more dependable the winds. To squeeze the maximum electricity out of any given resource, therefore, it is better to put up a machine that has its nose into the breeze at 150 metres, rather than at 80 metres. This has become the norm across Germany, Denmark and Sweden but Scotland has lagged behind, in part because there has been a widely-held assumption among planners and stakeholders that the landscape cannot accommodate larger machines. This is now changing with some local authorities, and elements within the Scottish government, flirting with a 'fewer but taller' approach.

Span is also essential. A turbine with blades of 75 metres captures much more wind than a turbine with blades of 50 metres, even when set at an equivalent height. It is of course possible to put very long blades on a tower only marginally taller by comparison, but not only would that scare the sheep with each downward swoop but it would also increase wear and tear on the wings due to ground-based turbulence as well as blowing up dirt and dust, increasing maintenance costs while also reducing efficiencies over time.

As a general rule, bigger blades and taller towers combine to produce more powerful machines. The industry standard during much of the RO era was for each turbine to produce between two and three megawatts, while projects build for the CfD regime more often than not featured machines of three to four megawatts. The new generation of post-subsidy projects are based on units of five megawatts and up, some developers have even applied for parameters that could accommodate units of seven megawatts, which manufacturers have yet to formally unveil.

The new generation of hardware also features an increased yield, ie it can on average produce more electricity from the same conditions than was previously the case. Over a year, for instance, rather than producing an average of 35 per cent of its nameplate capacity, a modern machine might be able to hit 40 per cent. The upfront investment in improved control systems, electrics etc will of course be more expensive, but over the lifetime of a wind farm, the overall returns will be much better.

Other elements will also contribute to cutting costs and increasing earnings. These include but certainly are not limited to improved operations and maintenance regimes and innovative finance packages that shave a few points off what was previously possible. In the 'subsidy free' world, any potential saving will be explored, any path to increased revenue will be considered.

How much cheaper will new wind need to be? Top of the range projects built in the final years of the RO were likely to produce a megawatt-hour of electricity for a cost in the neighbourhood of £55 to £65, if it was a quality effort. Those being planned for the post subsidy era will be looking to cut that significantly to around £35 to £40 per megawatt-hour.

Development activity towards that end, as measured by new planning applications, started to pick up in late 2018 after a few fallow years and increased through 2019. Some of this was down to strategic thinking (read wishful, perhaps) by companies expecting a change of government and/or policy and so a fresh approach to the onshore wind sector. Others have adopted an 'inevitability' position built on the expectation that the demand for green electricity and the relatively cheap cost of onshore when compared to competing technologies will make the sector impossible to ignore in the longer term. Both, as it happens, turned out to be right.

A larger proportion of activity is connected to projects designed to build under any circumstances, even if that is a complete vacuum of energy market policy. Many are chasing what are known as corporate power purchase agreements, a straightforward agreement between a generator and a buyer in which power from a wind farm is sold at a fixed price over a set period. The number of potential customers in this pool is relatively small, however, given they must combine a significant energy appetite, be willing to offer a long-term commitment, and be happy to establish a pricing regime at the outset. The potential to bundle a number of these corporate PPAs into one deal, so supporting a larger wind farm and perhaps spreading the risk of one buyer dropping out, is also being explored. Banks have been very wary of providing finance to these untested models but a small number have managed to get funding packages over the finishing line, sometimes it must be said completely sidestepping outside finance, and from that point on to building new wind farms.

ScottishPower is one of those to have squared the circle. The utility company in late 2019 announced construction of a pair of medium-scale onshore wind farms, one in Argyll and one in Caithness, with power to be sold to global online giant Amazon and UK supermarket chain Tesco. The breakthrough is the first by a utility in the post-subsidy world and, according to ScottishPower, highlights 'one of the options to activating investment in new green energy infrastructure from the corporate sector'. Compatriot utility SSE is busy building an extension to an existing wind farm in the Highlands on a merchant basis, selling power into the wider electricity market without the back-stop of a guaranteed long-term contract.

London investment company Greencoat, meanwhile,

MYTH 10

Wind is divisive

In a political sense, the Scottish Parliament has since its inception been positively disposed towards renewable energy, including onshore and offshore wind, with targets regularly increased over time, on a cross-party basis and often unanimously. Public attitude surveys regularly show high support for renewables in general, wind as a technology and onshore wind specifically.

is taking a portfolio approach to newbuild wind which essentially teams a subsidy-free project with a CfD winner to create an acceptable returns profile of roughly eight per cent across the combined entity; it is funding the venture off balance sheet so saving the cost of finance, and offloading the majority of construction risk to the original developer. The Greencoat route is likely to be copied by others but given it is tailored to the advantages inherent in what is an established, experienced and well-funded operator, the method is unlikely to be replicated other than by a few companies in very similar market circumstances.

The Conservative government elected in the General Election of December 2019, led by Boris Johnson, reversed the 2015 ban on UK onshore wind in the CfD auctions, starting in 2021 and against a background of rising global concerns about global warming.

Proposed wind farms across the Scottish mainland, as well as those designed to produce power on the fringes of the open market, will once again be encouraged to bid into a competitive process that promises successful participants a route to consumers. It should not be described as a subsidy, as prices are expected to hover around the wholesale cost of electricity. That means depending on market fluctuations, some weeks a wind farm top-up will be required, other weeks the wholesale price will apply. Winning onshore projects will go live through the end of the decade, once again joining their offshore counterparts in the list of Westminster's favoured technologies; CfD auctions are expected to continue on a rolling basis every other year and projects will reflect the efficiencies and streamlining already in train, but further honed during the sector's years in the wilderness.

What remains less clear at this point is the context for the promised rebirth of onshore wind and the continued expansion of offshore, the more specific end-goals and more systematic pathways required, rather than the current approach of 'let's produce a lot of low-carbon electricity and see what happens'. That green stock-piling is a necessary step, certainly; a fully-formed policy... probably not.

That is a matter for concern because we have been here before, when the hell-for-leather approach of the RO era created the backlash that eventually banished UK onshore wind into purgatory and put the industry into a tailspin. It is a matter of regret because it indicates through incomplete action a failure of government – and, by default, society – to address in a responsible way one of the greatest challenges of our times.

Welcome to the climate emergency.

12

The Turbine on the Hill

DRIVING NORTH FROM Inverness on the main road towards Dingwall, and eventually farther flung parts of the north and west Highlands, it is impossible to miss the turbine spinning atop a steep-sided hummock of a small hill above the farmland surrounding the Cromarty Firth. This is not a utility-scale generator in an upland plateau, but a piece of relatively human-scale technology designed to offset consumption some-where in the immediate locality of the valley floor, probably an agricultural holding.

The turbine stands starkly but elegantly white against what is a verdant background, even in winter, and I cannot recall a time – and I drive by fairly often – when it was not spinning happily on its horizontal axis, shipping power to some enterprise that itself is shaping the landscape through endeavours that in one form or another extend back in time for thousands of years. The machine is integrated into its surroundings and even those who campaign against wind would be forced to acknowledge that it seems part of its landscape, rather than standing out against it. You might as well be offended by a cow or a barn.

On the horizon, higher into the hills, is a smear of wind turbines that are by dint of distance tiny by comparison. There are a number of operational projects up there, of various vintages, so it is difficult to nail down exactly what you are looking at. Suffice to say all the candidates feature truly commercial-scale machines that stretch hundreds of feet into the air and produce enough power to make an impact on the national stage, not just on the scattered 'host' communities, farms and estates of Easter Ross and Sutherland. From a distance and from low altitudes it can be difficult to find the small gently rotating forms, even if you know they are there. Planning officials, anti-wind campaigners and development companies will disagree on the effectiveness of the intention, but all wind farms are in fact designed to make as minimal a landscape and visual impact as possible. Within the constraints of being enormous bits of metal in RAL 9016 Traffic White or a similarly designated shade of paint.

Scotland as a country travelled from scattered examples of the farm-scale turbine to thousands of megawatts of the utility vision of a wind farm in less than 25 years; it went from a nationwide grid-connected fleet capable of meeting zero per cent of electricity demand in 1995 to one that on a good day can now supply the equivalent of 100 per cent of power consumed north and south, east and west, islands and all. Detractors will say 'what went wrong?' but many lean towards the assessment of wind veteran Ted Leeming: 'That's some statement, the biggest you can get. In less than 30 years. That's powerful.'

Let that sink in: an electricity sector completely supplied by renewables. Put aside, for a moment, the background debate about costs, system issues such as grid and back-up, wild land impacts, noise, carbon payback, the jobs benefit or otherwise, the destination of profits, the motivations of developers, city money, nimbys and antis. Consider a world in which the kettle goes on, the phone is 100 per cent, the EV car is charged, the hospital lights are shining, heavy industry is supplied with electricity. All for essentially zero fuel cost, with nothing going into the front end of the pipe: no coal, no gas, no oil, no uranium. Forever. And nothing out the back end either: no particulates, no carbon, no nuclear waste. Fantasyland, right?

Of course, the reality is not that simple and all sides of the equation must certainly be considered as completely as

Spinning class: the turbine on the hill, in this specific case near Dingwall in the Scottish Highlands.
© Todd Westbrook

possible – good, bad, ugly – as Scotland decides how best to move forward against the background of the official climate emergency. Any discussion should, however, take place within that vision of what the wind sector at its core represents, of why that turbine – why any turbine – is on that hill: the provision of electricity with a minimal carbon footprint, at the lowest possible cost, as part of a system designed to maximise the effectiveness and efficiency of the electricity produced.

And the discussion needs to happen now. Ted Leeming again: 'In 2025, there will be no more UK coal, in 2040 there will be no more diesel or petrol cars. Electrification of transport will be over and above existing demands. Somebody has to come up with an integrated climate change policy incorporating all elements of heat, energy and transport that gets people building plant. And with Scotland the renewable energy capital of Europe we can continue to lead and inspire on a global stage. The climate tipping point is only years away. We have to start doing something radical immediately, just as we did all those years ago.'

The generation numbers bear another mention. Scotland's nuclear fleet currently provides around 28 per cent of electricity but is due to be shut down by the end of the 2020s. Gas, coal and oil provide 13 per cent of generation and will continue to decrease through the next decade. Simultaneously, the increase in expected electrification of the transport and heat sectors will increase the gigawatt-hours necessary to fuel everyday life; predictions vary wildly but estimates of six to seven times the current total annual generation totals are not unusual. There is going to be a massive hole to fill.

Much of the hard preparatory work has been done. A culture shift has been achieved on a national scale with utilities and network companies moving away from generally anti-renewables positions of the 1990s to one in which they have embraced and now actively promote, if not lead, the sector. Scotland and the wider UK hosts a legacy fleet of wind projects pumping out electricity on a scale to rival fossil fuel plants; technology is advancing at pace; the infrastructure necessary to shift power from one end of the country to the other, and across oceans, is partially ready and expanding rapidly; the ability to store significant volumes of power is increasing; expertise to maximise what new wind projects can and should offer is found among developers, contractors, planners and stakeholders – even though they may not always agree on the specific merits or otherwise of individual developments.

So what does Scotland need to do now? There are infinite ways to answer that question. My two cents' worth follows but please debate, challenge and differ; as indicated at the outset of this book, I am no expert. This is, however, a discussion that needs to be had at a societal level, so consider this part of a ball now rolling.

1. Keep the fleet spinning

Scotland has an onshore wind fleet of around 8,000 megawatts that in parts is starting to come to the end of its operational life. The main options for ageing projects include decommissioning, lifetime extension, repowering with more modern turbines, or some combination. It would represent a backward step if the zero-carbon projects already in place and providing 'green' electricity were taken off the network, so with the exception of egregious planning mistakes (I can think of a few off the top of my head, but only a few), the existing generating plant must be retained.

Lifetime extension of five or ten years will work at some locations, depending on the economics involved and against the background of ongoing improvements to operations and maintenance regimes, but the more likely option for the majority of ageing wind farms is repowering with new, more advanced wind turbines. Onshore technology has made great strides in recent years with costs coming down, reliability and efficiency going up. New projects, even at the exact same nameplate capacity and within the same height constraints, will produce more power more dependably from the exact same site.

Fewer but larger machines is the most likely template for most repowering projects and while some will be concerned about landscape impacts, the lesson from more mature markets – Denmark and Germany, largely – is that viewsheds are improved by replacing many small machines with a reduced number of larger ones. Wind veteran Ray Hunter, who we first met in Chapter Four, is among those arguing that the big beasts will quickly become commonplace. 'There are places where they shouldn't go, but the reality is that industry is very good about avoiding those. I would compare views about accepting larger turbines with television sizes. A 32-inch screen used to be a really big TV; now it doesn't even register.'

So in summary: keep what Scotland already has, but make it better. Much money and effort has been spent building the collective onshore wind fleet, upgrading and expanding the grid network needed to make the best use of its generation, and solving associated hurdles such as radar interference. There will be the inevitable technical issues with repowering – what to do about redundant foundations and roads etc – but these are secondary and should be acknowledged as such.

2. Make a decision about the future energy mix

Scotland as a country must make strategic decisions about how it will provide the energy required to supply the electricity, heat and transport necessary to maintain its lifestyles and economy while simultaneously addressing net-zero emissions. Recent history has shown that establishing a Scotland-centric plan might be difficult given the sometimes disparate policy paths of governments in Edinburgh and London, but this should not become a constitutional issue; this country must act whether

MYTH 11

Wind affects house prices

There is no evidence that houses near wind farms experience a reduction in value. Some studies have indicated that prices can be impacted during construction, or during heated arguments about a specific potential project, but tend to rebound very soon afterwards (when people wonder what the fuss was all about).

it is independent, in some sort of federal UK, with devo max, or under the status quo. The exact means available under those various scenarios will differ but the ends must be the same, and time must not be wasted arguing that 'if only x, we could do y'. Work with the tools you have, until you have something different.

Conversations must result in a broad framework and direction: for instance it could be decided that power will be generated in a few large plants and shipped around the country, it might be 100 per cent decentralised with each community responsible for ensuring it has the energy it needs, it could include the export of green electricity and import of hydrogen fuels, it can be a combination of any of those or none. Difficult questions will have to be asked about Scotland's oil and gas sector, about businesses processing or reliant on hydrocarbons, about special treatments for energy-intensive but job-rich industries. Be prepared for the tendrils of the issue to stretch into all parts of life: public transport, built infrastructure, air travel and agriculture to name but a few.

And no wishful thinking: it is easy to say carbon capture and storage will solve all of our problems in one fell swoop, but CCS is nowhere near being a commercial option. Ditto with tidal or wave power and with nuclear fusion. Energy efficiency can only go so far, EV cars are not the only answer, houses leaking heat will take time and money to replace, newbuild nukes takes at least ten years and there is still no satisfactory answer to dealing with the waste. All those things could come good in time, but not tomorrow. Those involved in the discussions about where Scotland goes next should be realistic and be prepared to both compromise and provide alternatives; just saying 'nope' isn't an option.

Also worth remembering that the market will work within any parameters created, but it cannot be expected to make decisions about the best way forward. There are some things governments have to do.

3. Decide what role wind has to play in the net-zero energy mix

Wind is a proven technology that can be deployed at a lower cost than other renewables and produce electricity in a broadly predictable, reliable but, yes, intermittent way – ie whenever the breeze is blowing. It can be combined with onsite storage, integrated with pump-storage hydro, exported via interconnectors. Onshore, it requires great big metal turbines to be constructed on concrete foundations, linked by tracks and connected to the grid by power lines. The better the wind resource the more electricity will be produced; projects in the Scottish context tend to be distant from population centres.

Some people don't like the way they look, some believe any proximity whatsoever desecrates mountain landscapes and other scenic areas, some like them as long as they are somewhere else. The most extreme Antis believe they are part of a global conspiracy, although to what exact end has never been disclosed. (I was once told by a campaigner that the industry was established so the concrete bases could be used to hide radioactive materials produced by unspecified shenanigans, but I think that was more of a sideshow and not the *main* conspiracy.)

Whatever your views, wind is a known quantity and therefore provides a largely surprise-free variable in wider discussions about energy and decarbonisation. The current policy of the Scottish government is to embrace deployment of additional onshore and offshore, and some many thousands of megawatts are waiting in the wings with planning permission but, as we have seen in previous chapters, the route to market for onshore has until very recently been strangled by decisions taken at Westminster.

Against the changing background, Scotland needs to make a decision about how a new generation of onshore wind fits the big-picture energy system established under point two.

Politicians and stakeholders need to agree some strategic and firm rules about where and under what circumstances new onshore wind projects should be built, and what limits in terms of capacity or geography there will be to that expansion. Should the country pursue a few large-scale arrays, should every community be incentivised – and be pre-permitted – to build its own turbine, should every factory offset its own power needs? And when will there be enough?

With a destination already in mind in terms of 'net-zero' by 2045, the detailed roadmap of how Scotland gets there is key. If the inevitable back and forth with Westminster is framed as a workable, long-term and detailed plan to meet the country's ambitious climate targets – agreed by a range of Scottish interests – it will be far more difficult to argue against; London is otherwise likely to follow its own well-beaten paths towards 'what the people want' in terms of renewables, rather than what matters north of the border.

4. Provide certainty through policy (rather than subsidy)

The SRO years in the 1990s pushed down prices too steeply, making auction winners in some cases impossible to build. The RO from 2002 to 2018 was wildly successful in terms of sparking both onshore and offshore deployment but also drove speculative development and unsustainable profit levels that created a public and political backlash. The CfD era is still too young, in terms of onshore wind on the mainland, to provide any firm evidence on longer-term development, construction and investment patterns; the jury remains out on any lessons from the ten onshore Scottish winners in that first auction round.

Where does the market go from here? In the immediate term, the revised CfD mechanism should provide certainty and some degree of comfort for investment in new projects onshore and continued expansion of the offshore wind sector.

No large-scale energy project – be it wind, gas, nuclear or other – can be achieved without the sort of business case certainty that will allow banks to provide multiple millions in funding, will allow boards to approve balance sheet spending on similar levels. Infrastructure depends on having faith that market conditions will be consistent over ten, 15 or 20 years; that environment can only be created by governments, with the exact levers depending very much on ideology. That the UK government has to date displayed a willingness to chop and change market conditions willy-nilly will not work in its favour.

Societal spending on onshore projects in the early years of the industry helped it to establish a commercial pedigree, to accelerate development in the face of the dominance of fossil fuels, to provide a foothold that allowed offshore wind, marine energy and other renewables the room to grow and in some cases reach maturity. All of us paid for the research and development stage of wind power through levies on consumer bills, but as of now we are not reaping the full rewards of that investment because of the lack of consistent policy support for the sector.

Wind is currently the cheapest way to supply large volumes of electricity to the grid, not just when compared to other renewables but across all technologies. However, governments at all levels must commit to a long-term policy landscape that provides certainty for developers, investors, the supply chain and adjacent enabling sectors such as grid, storage, hydrogen and electric vehicles. It is not enough to say 'we should all be green, go make it happen'; create the framework, and do so at no extra cost to consumers. It is more than possible.

5. Be honest and communicate

There is little point pretending everyone will be happy with the decisions that need to be taken about a new generation of wind power. The sector will inevitably feel the future is too restrictive in comparison to the boom years, while some opposition elements will decry any newbuild, whether onshore or offshore and under whatever circumstances. Rival renewable energy technologies will feel ignored even if they know in their collective hearts they are not ready to produce power on a commercial scale; the fossil fuel generators will argue they have a part to play without going too far into the details of how they will tackle the emissions issue; nuclear is likely to feel demonised, but then it should be used to that.

The blunt reality is the climate emergency necessitates some difficult choices, which under other circumstances and in other times might have been deemed unpalatable: the rapid end of petrol or diesel cars, curbs on air travel, restrictions on oil and gas exploration. Others might list as undesirable a shift to more onshore wind, increased transmission infrastructure, newbuild large-scale pumped-storage hydro, solar panels on every rooftop, emission-free zones and mandatory public transport corridors.

Trade-offs will be necessary. It could be onshore wind has a limited role in Scotland's energy future, perhaps offshore wind can do the trick, but that must be an active decision rather than relying on the market to determine the outcome. Underplaying onshore is frankly akin to leaving your most productive cash crop unplanted and allowing those fields to go fallow but, to squeeze another drop from the metaphor, if that is the policy selected then at least do so on the basis that you have food available elsewhere.

Decisions must in all cases be communicated effectively and honestly. All actions must be placed in a longer-term context (with 2045 in mind, I would argue), reasonable arguments put forward to support conclusions, realistic budgets produced, potential knock-on impacts explained; do not pull any punches and, at this point, why bother sugar-coating anything? Conversations with the electorate should be approached by political parties as if all concerned are adults acting in the best interest of the country and for the generations to come. Even if some are nowhere near that grown up.

6. Share the wealth

There is an opportunity for Scotland to make the most of its natural resources, in much the same way that Norway has managed its oil and gas wealth (and which the UK manifestly failed to do). The new national investment bank has a role to play, state-owned landowners are key, perhaps auction rounds will be required to win licences for future development, so providing a return to the country as a whole. It is ultimately a question of control – of policy, or resource. Of reward.

Wind veteran Ray Hunter believes the time has come. 'For Scotland it is important we decide how we handle future development. We've got the resource, it is exploitable, we can do more than we've done to date; heat and transport are huge opportunities. There is an increasing demand, there are oodles of natural resources. Scotland is in a state of flux and the energy industry has a role to play in where it goes next,' he said.

'It is up to politicians to decide who enjoys the profits from wind. Should the Scottish nation have an investment in ownership, supply, finance? Yes it should. That should not be a radical suggestion but the answer to date is that it has not happened. [Looking to the future] we have the benefits of hindsight, we have the resources, we have the open goal. Just shoot.'

You heard the man. Just shoot.

Much of the country's wind sector, despite the limbo of recent years, is more than ready for what comes next. The people and the skills are still there; for some of those involved, this author is relieved to report on the back of the many months of research necessary to pull together this book, it is still about changing the world.

Jonathan Hill, who helped to build Scotland's first wind farm at Hagshaw Hill in the mid-1990s, described the then embryonic industry in terms that remain relevant to many parts even today: 'We worked 60, sometimes 65-hour weeks. No overtime, none of that gloss. We were doing it because we wanted to.'

Turbine sales guru Mark Powell echoed the sentiment: 'It was a moral thing to be in, so it was great to be involved with a source of energy that used a fuel that didn't cost anything. At that point it was not structured, not corporate, it was all down to the people. A collection of individuals that worked together to achieve something.

'You felt empowered, out there making the chances. And the industry knew that the UK was this amazing place for wind.'

Stuart Hall, another pioneer with links to Hagshaw, also believes the revolutionary spirit which drove the initial projects can help push wind into a new era, even if the majority of the hard digging is over and those metaphorical spades of the early efforts retired gracefully to the shed.

'My work is done; as far as large-scale wind in Scotland is concerned it is now a mainstream business,' he said. 'In the early days, the very sort of people we didn't like are the ones we needed to get involved: oil and gas, utilities, big manufacturers. I'm interested in making change, in the passion of doing something you really believe in. With wind power, it is now cemented within big business and going to happen.'

Hall believes the visionaries with the strongest creative drive, that urge to change the world, will be attracted into initiatives designed to facilitate increased penetration of wind power and other renewables into the energy mix, will be drawn to efforts to shift the economy firmly onto a zero-carbon footing.

'If you are that type of person, some elements of wind power are a good place to be but, because it involves big corporates, there is always the chance an element of greed

Scottish Electricity Consumption vs Wind Generation

2004

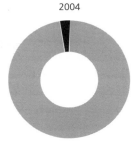

■ Total consumption: 34,845 GWh   ■ Wind generation: 848 GWh (2%)

2010

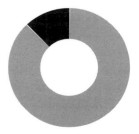

■ Total consumption: 33,144 GWh   ■ Wind generation: 4,933 GWh (13%)

2018

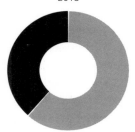

■ Total consumption: 29,711 GWh   ■ Wind generation: 19,336 GWh (39%)

NOTE: Wind generation figures are bundled with a
tiny percentage of wave and solar output.
Source: UK Government (BEIS).

will come in,' he said. 'If you want to make a difference, wind [farm development] is perhaps not the place to be. Storage, load management, there are lots of other opportunities for innovation in wind power that would be better.'

Technologies that allow for renewables to directly displace fossil fuels in the system, so allowing renewables to be at their best and achieve their full potential, are particularly important, he said.

Beatrice demonstration project veteran Dietmar Gosch's advice, for offshore at least, is to take advantage of the experiences already garnered in adjacent sectors. 'I'm a strong believer in renewables but you have to thank the people from the industry that helped humans to develop for more than a century: the future has to be in renewables, but the people from the oil and gas sector are very good and professional in the offshore environment. That's where we learn from one another.'

And there is of course undeniable potential for the offshore side of the wind equation both for floating and fixed structures and around all coasts. For Scotland, it is a part of the industry that could grow exponentially through this decade and the next – think in tens of gigawatts, rather than thousands of megawatts – and provide a significant boost to decarbonisation efforts. However, it must be remembered that, however promising, the sector is young in a Scottish context and faces stiff competition from mega-projects in waters south of the border and all around the North Sea. Much must still go right for the reality to match some of the rhetoric – in terms of policy, planning, supply chain and deployment – and for the proven deliverability of the onshore wind workhorse, however unsexy by comparison, to translate fully into its offshore counterpart.

For it is on land where the soul of the Scottish renewables sector first developed, building on the hydro revolution that famously brought power to the glens in the 1940s and 1950s. Hunter again: 'Onshore wind has not come and gone, it will continue. The sites that have been developed will not disappear when they reach the end of their first round life. We're not in that zone yet, but what was good and right about the first round should benefit the second round.'

He also acknowledges the changed cost profile and the public need to see value for money, which makes the economic argument as strong as the climate one. 'It is now affordable. It wasn't under the SRO, it wasn't under the RO. It is now, and no longer needs support. England doesn't need to subsidise us, renewables just needs market access and it can be a price setter.'

The coming era in Scotland, according to one vision for the industry, is an expanding onshore and offshore wind fleet managed as part of a nationwide energy strategy that combines grid networks, EV charging, active management of power flows and battery and pump storage. It is the diversified, self-contained Orkney approach on a large stage, it is the Shetland desire for local control combined with benefits for all, it is the hippie heart of Hagshaw and samba bands and tie-dye shirts applied to big climate questions, corporate profitability and practical management of abundant natural resources.

EW Golding, the energy visionary who we met at the start of this book, would hardly recognise the modern landscape of Scottish wind power, the strides taken since he erected his prototype on Orkney as autumn turned to winter in 1951. Turbines that can be ten times as tall, 100 times more powerful, arranged in arrays that stretch across mountain tops, rise above the oceans, float in deep waters; enough electricity produced on a windy day to power an entire country; a nationwide fuel mix that often includes no coal and decreasing amounts of gas and nuclear.

The Englishman would nevertheless be familiar with some of the arguments still raging about wind's role and effectiveness, about its place in our lives. What would he make of the global warming debate, of demands for carbon reduction, of Scottish plans to hit net-zero by 2045? What would he say about the potential of electricity storage, about international interconnection, about smart grids and charging points? What would he think of the Antis, of the spread of wind-related myths, of demonising in parts of the national press? How would he judge Chris Heaton-Harris and the Conservative Party, Labour and the LibDems, the Scottish National Party, the Scottish Greens?

As man of science, Golding could probably have been relied upon to look at the facts, to ignore the hoo-ha and weigh the alternatives, the good and the bad, the pros and the cons. Wind is not the saviour but nor is it the antichrist; it is, like all things made by man, a tool. How and whether we use any tool says more about ourselves – our judgments, our ambitions, our fears, even our morality – than about the implement itself.

The turbine on the hill produces electricity by harnessing the power of the wind. From that point on, it is pretty much up to us to decide what happens next.

Postscript

NEARLY A QUARTER of a century has passed since the first commercial wind farm in Scotland was built at Hagshaw Hill in South Lanarkshire and the endgame for those 26 Bonus turbines is now in sight. Long-time landowner Mitchell & Sons has been given permission to repower the site near Douglas with what it describes as a 46 per cent decrease in turbine numbers and a 520 per cent increase in energy production.

Replacement machines will of course be much larger; the existing fleet of 55-metre high structures will under the proposals be decommissioned to clear the way for hardware nearly four times taller at 200 metres. The next-generation turbines will wander across the existing project footprint on Hagshaw, Common and Broomerside hills as well as additional acreage to the south of the current project, alongside the Galawhistle wind farm (built in the interim).

Plans form part of wider ambitions labelled as the Hagshaw Wind Cluster and were acquired by ScottishPower in 2020. In addition to the repowering, the development will also include the ongoing operations at Hagshaw Hill 2 and a separate nearby development at Douglas. Cranes and bulldozers will soon return to the site to begin what sholud be the first end-of-life repowering in the country.

Full circle.

Long-time turbine salesman Claus Poulsen, although not involved at Hagshaw, sees a certain elegance in the proceedings: 'That's the beauty of this industry,' he said of the graceful replacement of older projects. 'Technology has moved so fast and repowering is part of that. There is a natural evolution at work.'

The rebirth at Hagshaw will also serve as an official

swansong for this correspondent as a 'Scottish wind guy', a full 16 years after I first phoned since-vanished developer Airtricity to ask about a proposal in Ayrshire and filed a story with the immortal line, cut by the subs, 'Sheep and rough-grazing cattle will remain on the site throughout the life of the project'. (Up to date images of the now 15-year-old turbine field above the Firth of Clyde seem to have borne that out, by the way.)

Information about wind farms, turbines, developers and developments across renewable technologies – in Scotland, but also around the globe – will no longer fill notebooks, itemised telephone bills, expenses claims, my professional life, my weekdays and sometimes even weekends and holidays.

I will remain curious about the turbine on the hill, about who built it and why, about the travels the project made through development and planning, the innovations deployed, who will profit and who will consume the electricity, which companies supplied and built it, who lobbied against and whether any metaphorical bodies were buried along the way.

But I will drive on, or walk by, without asking the usual shopping list of questions. Wind has morphed from a 'when, where, why, who and how' into a simple 'is': an element in the built landscape, one factor among many to be considered when discussing how best to power our homes and industry, one piece of the climate emergency puzzle, a normal part of modern life.

That is enough for me, the reporter's notebook labelled 'wind power' is closed. There is other human endeavour to document.

I look forward to meeting you on that journey.

Todd Westbrook
Strathspey, Scotland,
September 2020

MYTH 12

Concrete turbine foundations are used to hide radioactive materials

Nope. Although it would be some story.

Acknowledgements

I WOULD LIKE to express my heartfelt appreciation to all of those who contributed to the making of this 'short, sharp history'. Many, many conversations were had through the research stage and – whether or not directly quoted – those exchanges without fail or exception added valuable information, insight, context and nuance to the narrative of what is a multi-faceted, complex and still-evolving story. There are some amazing people doing incredible things in green energy practice, policy and governance; those who spoke or corresponded with me could not have been more generous with their time and patience, so many thanks to all.

Much appreciation is also due to the archivists, librarians and self-described wind geeks who provided or pointed the way to original source materials, particularly from the earliest years of the sector in Scotland. A lot of documentation is not readily available or accessible so having those experienced guides through the digital and physical remnants of this particular industry's history was a huge help.

My publisher Luath Press has been fantastic from start to finish; thanks to all on the team in Edinburgh for having faith in this project from the earliest stages, and for providing the expertise necessary to transform a manuscript reeking of 'life-long journalist' into a publishable work.

Finally, and most fundamentally, thanks to my wife and my girls for believing that this could come to pass, for making the sacrifices necessary for that to happen and for pretending throughout that I am not in fact a pain in the ass. And to my dog, who forced me at least twice a day to get away from the desk and to experience the rain, snow, sleet and rare sun of the Highlands.

Some Useful Websites

Scottish Government
www.gov.scot/energy/

Scottish Government Energy Consents Unit
www.energyconsents.scot/ApplicationSearch.aspx

NatureScot
www.nature.scot

UK Dept for Business, Energy & Industrial Strategy
www.gov.uk/government/organisations/department-for-business-energy-and-industrial-strategy

UK Low Carbon Contracts Company
www.lowcarboncontracts.uk

Scottish Renewables
www.scottishrenewables.com

RenewableUK
www.renewableuk.com

WindEurope
windeurope.org

Global Wind Energy Council
gwec.net

IEA
www.iea.org

Climatexchange
www.climatexchange.org.uk

Offshore Wind Scotland
www.offshorewindscotland.org.uk

John Muir Trust
www.johnmuirtrust.org/latest

Mountaineering Scotland
www.mountaineering.scot/news

BBC
www.bbc.co.uk/news/topics/c008ql151g1t/wind-power

WUWT
wattsupwiththat.com

EnergyWatch
energywatch.eu

reNEWS
renews.biz

GTM
www.greentechmedia.com

Windpower Monthly
www.windpowermonthly.com/news

Carbon Brief
www.carbonbrief.org

Scotland Against Spin
scotlandagainstspin.org

Some other books published by **Luath Press**

The Hydro Boys
Emma Wood
ISBN 1 84282 047 8 PBK £8.99

'I heard about drowned farms and hamlets, the ruination of the salmon-fishing and how Inverness might be washed away if the dams failed inland. I was told about the huge veins of crystal they found when they were tunnelling deep under the mountains and when I wanted to know who "they" were, what stories I got in reply!'

The hydro-electric project was a crusade, with a marvellous goal: the prize of affordable power for all from Scottish rainfall. This book is a journey through time, and across and beneath the Highland landscape. Nobody should forget the human sacrifice made by those who built the dams all those years ago. The politicians, engineers and navvies of the era bequeathed to us the major source of renewable energy down to the present day.

Tunnel Tigers
Patrick Campbell
ISBN 1 84282 072 9 PBK £8.99

Tunnel tigers belong to an elite group of construction workers who specialise in a highly paid but dangerous profession: driving tunnels through mountains or underneath rivers or other large bodies of water.

In the 1940s and 1950s, they were involved in a score of huge hydroelectric tunnels in Pitlochry and the Highlands of Scotland. They continue with their dangerous craft today in various locations all over the world.

Tunnel Tigers is a colourful portrait of the off-beat characters who worked on the Scottish projects, and of the tensions that were created when men of various religious and ethnic groups shared the same space.

Details of these and other books published by **Luath Press** can be found at:
www.luath.co.uk

Luath Press Limited

committed to publishing well written books worth reading

LUATH PRESS takes its name from Robert Burns, whose little collie Luath (*Gael.*, swift or nimble) tripped up Jean Armour at a wedding and gave him the chance to speak to the woman who was to be his wife and the abiding love of his life. Burns called one of the 'Twa Dogs' Luath after Cuchullin's hunting dog in Ossian's *Fingal*. Luath Press was established in 1981 in the heart of Burns country, and is now based a few steps up the road from Burns' first lodgings on Edinburgh's Royal Mile. Luath offers you distinctive writing with a hint of unexpected pleasures.

Most bookshops in the UK, the US, Canada, Australia, New Zealand and parts of Europe, either carry our books in stock or can order them for you. To order direct from us, please send a £sterling cheque, postal order, international money order or your credit card details (number, address of cardholder and expiry date) to us at the address below. Please add post and packing as follows: UK – £1.00 per delivery address; overseas surface mail – £2.50 per delivery address; overseas airmail – £3.50 for the first book to each delivery address, plus £1.00 for each additional book by airmail to the same address. If your order is a gift, we will happily enclose your card or message at no extra charge.

Luath Press Limited
543/2 Castlehill
The Royal Mile
Edinburgh EH1 2ND
Scotland
Telephone: +44 (0)131 225 4326 (24 hours)
Email: sales@luath. co.uk
Website: www.luath.co.uk